The Economics of Regional Water Quality Management

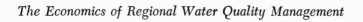

THE ECONOMICS OF REGIONAL WATER QUALITY MANAGEMENT

By Allen V. Kneese

PUBLISHED FOR RESOURCES FOR THE FUTURE, INC.
By The Johns Hopkins Press, Baltimore

RESOURCES FOR THE FUTURE, INC.

1755 Massachusetts Avenue, N.W., Washington, D.C. 20036

Board of Directors, Reuben G. Gustavson, Chairman, Horace M. Albright, Erwin
D. Canham, Thomas H. Carroll, E. J. Condon (Honorary), Joseph L. Fisher,
Luther H. Foster, Hugh L. Keenleyside, Otto H. Liebers, Leslie A. Miller,
Frank Pace, Jr., William S. Paley, Laurance S. Rockefeller, Stanley H. Rut-
tenberg, John W. Vanderwilt, P. F. Watzek

President, Joseph L. Fisher

Vice President, Irving K. Fox

Secretary-Treasurer, John E. Herbert

Resources for the Future is a non-profit corporation for research and education
in the development, conservation, and use of natural resources. It was established in 1952 with the co-operation of the Ford Foundation and its activities
since then have been financed by grants from that Foundation. Part of the work
of Resources for the Future is carried out by its resident staff, part supported
by grants to universities and other non-profit organizations. Unless otherwise
stated, interpretations and conclusions in RFF publications are those of the
authors; the organization takes responsibility for the selection of significant
subjects for study, the competence of the researchers, and their freedom of inquiry.

This book is one of RFF's water resources studies, which are directed by
Allen V. Kneese.

RFF publications staff: Henry Jarrett, *editor;* Vera W. Dodds, *associate editor;*
Nora E. Roots, *assistant editor.*

Preface

How clean should a stream be? And what represents an efficient way of bringing about desired conditions?

These are the basic issues that confront those who are concerned with the husbandry of water resources through pollution control. At least this is how it appears to me as an engineer who has been engaged in the planning and execution of such endeavors. And now it is my privilege to write a preface to a book in which these issues are addressed from the viewpoint of an economist.

During the past year I have been on leave to serve as a member of the staff of Resources for the Future, Inc. For an engineer it was a rewarding experience to be exposed to the outlook of social scientists and to share in their "way of thinking," notably with respect to the reconciliation of conflicts in water use. This has added to an appreciation of the manner in which Allen Kneese, an associate in RFF and the author of this book, has clarified concepts of pollution control policy and practice by examining them within the context of welfare economics.

Dr. Kneese's contribution is significant and unique. It is significant because it gives form and substance to the heretofore nebulous concept of water quality management. It is unique in that it provides specific illustration of how theory and methodology of resources allocation may be employed in the formulation of rational decisions affecting water use and reuse.

In recent years, the term "water quality management" has been advanced as offering a more precise and positive description of the goal of pollution control effort. But notions of what it should encompass and how it might be implemented have lacked definition and structure. Equally illusive has been an understanding of how economic analysis and optimization techniques might be applied in the design of a comprehensive water supply-waste disposal system.

Acknowledgment of these deficiencies is found in a principal recommendation emanating from the 1960 National Conference on Water Pollution, where it was asserted:

> There is need for a more systematic approach to the evaluation of water pollution problems to include health, aesthetic and market values. A framework of analysis must be developed which will provide a relatively precise understanding of benefit-cost and which will form the basis for the design of public policies and programs for effective water quality management.

Dr. Kneese's book does even more than satisfy this challenging assignment. He has developed a conceptual basis and outlined procedures for planning a management program tailored to the physical, hydrological, and economic circumstances of a watershed. What is unfolded is a systematic approach to solving the problem of maintaining conditions in a river that will yield the greatest over-all net benefits. Attention is directed not only to the engineering and economic aspects of such an undertaking, but also to the institutional arrangements required for its execution.

With respect to this latter point, it becomes apparent that existing state and federal administrative machinery, which is geared primarily to the exercise of regulatory functions often based on rule-of-thumb standards, is hardly suited for the more exacting task of achieving optimal use of streams. This mechanism provides little or no opportunity to choose from among a variety of technological alternatives and to carry out those best fitted to minimize the detrimental effects and the costs associated with waste disposal. Neither are conditions propitious for consideration of the niceties of cost allocation and the application of incentives by means of effluent charges and subsidies. Incidentally, the effluent-charge philosophy espoused by Dr. Kneese should be recognized by sanitary engineers as a sophisticated application to an entire river system of the principle of waste-load surcharges, which is favored by many municipalities for sharing costs of treatment facilities among industrial users of this service and for encouraging reduction of pollution loads at their source. Likewise, the discussion on subsidy payments should be regarded as offering a more rational approach for providing incentives for pollution abatement than is possible under present procedures in allocating federal and state grants for this purpose.

Not the least of the virtues of the book is the direction it furnishes for the expression of public policy with respect to pollution control. The social aim of such endeavors has been characterized by uncertainty. On the one hand, there are some who would tolerate an attitude of unconcern about pollution until a nuisance is created. At the other extreme are those who assert that users of water should return it to streams as clean as "technically" possible. In between these viewpoints regarding the appropriate condition of streams— which range from acceptance of foulness to aspirations for pristine purity—an accommodation must be sought. We are not confronted with a question of absolutes—of clean water versus dirty water or of fish versus factories—but one of efficient adjustment to water reuse. A reasonable basis for decision-making is to be found in weighing the benefits and costs of maintaining various levels of river quality. Dr. Kneese shows the possibilities of making such an analysis and the promise of devising a combination of measures to attain the quality desired at least cost.

There are other reasons for applauding the content and timeliness of this book. One is that the federal government is now embarking on multimillion dollar comprehensive planning projects for abatement of pollution. Rewards from such efforts will be enhanced if the concepts of water quality management and the analytical techniques associated with it receive full consideration. Thus the investigations would be oriented to yield not "a plan" for a river basin but a group of alternative choices with a price tag attached to each.

Still another reason for welcoming the book is that it furnishes guidelines for research in the economic and managerial sciences, as well as in the physical sciences, to promote development of river quality management techniques. For example, the measurement of penalties associated with quality impairment claims attention. Assessment of health and recreational benefits presents a challenging problem. Information is needed on both water and waste treatment costs, notably with respect to industrial activities. And experimentation should be encouraged with institutional devices to test their suitability for basin-wide integration of planning, design, construction, and operating functions. Some of this research has already been started by Resources for the Future, Inc.

It would be doing an injustice to Allen Kneese if this preface implies that his book is a compendium of quick and easy answers for solving the pollution problem. What he has produced is a scholarly treatise that probes basic questions and from which emerges the rationale for developing appropriate answers. His identification and analysis of the physical and economic interdependencies associated with water use reveal the practical possibilities for planning solutions within a systems context. This is an important book. From it we can learn how to sharpen existing tools and shape new ones to extract maximum net benefits from a limited resource.

EDWARD J. CLEARY
Executive Director and Chief Engineer
Ohio River Valley Water Sanitation Commission

Cincinnati, Ohio
May, 1964

Acknowledgments

The list of people to whom I am indebted for help is a long one that reflects the variety of disciplines which play a role in dealing with water quality management problems.

Foremost among those who have rendered assistance are Irving K. Fox and John V. Krutilla of the water resources section at Resources for the Future, Inc. Orris C. Herfindahl, of RFF, and Jerome Milliman, of Indiana University, who was on leave with RFF while most of the writing was being done, provided valuable suggestions and constructive reviews of various drafts of the manuscript. Marion Clawson, Robert K. Davis, and Jack L. Knetsch of RFF and Edward J. Cleary, on leave from the Ohio River Valley Sanitation Commission, also read an entire draft and contributed useful suggestions.

Numerous persons outside RFF also reviewed all or portions of the manuscript and suggested many helpful changes. Prominent among them were Jacob H. Beuscher, School of Law, University of Wisconsin; Blair Bower, Department of Economics and Civil Engineering, University of New Mexico; Emery N. Castle, Department of Agricultural Economics, University of Oregon; Fred Clarenbach, Department of Urban and Regional Planning, University of Wisconsin; Lyle E. Craine, School of Natural Resources, Department of Conservation, University of Michigan; Otto Davis, School of Industrial Administration, Carnegie Institute of Technology; B. H. Dieterich, Community Water Supply, Division of Environmental Health, World Health Organization, Geneva; Gordon M. Fair, Department of Sanitary Engineering, Harvard University; Louis M. Falkson, Department of Economics, Harvard University; Richard J. Frankel, Department of Civil Engineering, University of California at Berkeley; M. Mason Gaffney, Department of Economics, University of Wisconsin; Karl Gertel, Farm Economics Research Division, Agricultural Research Service, U.S. Department of Agriculture; Maynard Hufschmidt, Water Resources Seminar, Harvard University; C. H. J. Hull, Department of Sanitary Engineering, Johns Hopkins University; Robert W. Kates, Graduate School of Geography, Clark University; Edgar Landenberger, U.S. Corps of Engineers, Washington, D.C.; Bernard C. McBeath, Engineering Economic Planning Program, Stanford University; Michael McGoldrick, Engineering Economic Planning Program, Stanford University; Frederick E. McJunkin, The School of Public Health, University of North Carolina; Carl A. Rambow, James M. Montgomery Consulting Engineers, Pasadena, California; Vernon W. Ruttan, Department of Agricultural Economics, Purdue University; Graham Waite, Department of Law, University of Maine; Eugene W. Weber, Office of the Chief of Engineers, U.S. Army; Burton Weisbrod, Industrial Relations Section, Princeton University; and Nathaniel Wollman, Department of Economics, University of New Mexico.

A special set of acknowledgments should be made for chapter 7, which deals with the *Genossenschaften* of the Ruhr area of Germany. Discussions with Gordon Fair of Harvard University, Edward J. Cleary, of the Ohio River Valley Sanitation Commission, and S. V. Ciriacy-Wantrup of the University of California have contributed to my education in matters of *Wasserwirtschaft* in the Ruhr area. Special thanks are due to H. W. Koenig, of the Ruhrverband-Ruhrtalsperrenverein, and E. Knop of the Emschergenossenschaft–Lippeverband, Heinz Klosterkemper of the Ministry of Food, Agriculture, and Forestry of Northrhine Westphalia. Not only did they provide a detailed critique of an earlier version of chapter 7, but they and their staffs gave many hours of their time for consultation and for extensive guided tours to points of interest in regard to water management in the Ruhr area. Officials of the Wupperverband, Niersverband, and Erftverband also gave generously of their time during my visits to their offices.

Despite the generous help of all these people, the author accepts full responsibility for any errors of fact or interpretation which may remain.

A.V.K.

Contents

~~~~~~

xi

The Economics of Regional Water Quality Management

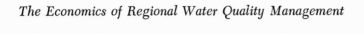

Part I

The Nature of the Problem

1

Introduction

~~~~~~

Interest in the problem of water quality is at a high pitch. Several sets of Congressional hearings on the matter have recently been held, a special committee of the Senate has in the past few years completed a monumental study of water resources with heavy emphasis on quality, and the daily press carries articles on one or another aspect of water pollution with great frequency. A number of national laws dealing with federal participation in pollution control activities have been passed in the past decade. The Federal Water Pollution Control Act amendments of 1961, for example, authorized the inclusion of water quality control storage in federal reservoirs. The U.S. Public Health Service has started to conduct comprehensive water quality investigations which will eventually include all of the river basins in the United States. State and interstate activities have been accelerated, and research pertinent to water quality in the natural sciences and engineering has expanded greatly in the past several years.

The pollution control efforts have already borne some fruit. Over the past ten years or so the condition of the main stems of some of our most heavily used streams has improved markedly. This is true, for example, of the Delaware, the Ohio and the Potomac; many of the highly offensive materials that once floated down these rivers are now removed from the effluents before they enter the stream. Nevertheless, serious problems of water quality still confront the nation. Their solution will call for a high level of interest and action by economists and public administrators as well as by biological and physical scientists and engineers. Indeed, the conviction that this is the case promoted the writing of this book.

There is ample evidence that the costs imposed upon water users through the discharge of wastes into water courses are large, and potential costs are increasing rapidly. In response to this situation, cities and industries have been required or induced to undertake enormous investments in waste disposal facilities.

It has long been evident that economic institutions on which we customarily rely to balance costs and returns—the interaction of market forces in a private enterprise system—do not perform this function satisfactorily for waste disposal. Aesthetic nuisance in a stream destroys public values that are not marketable. In deciding how to dispose of its wastes, an upstream firm or city is not forced to take into account the costs imposed upon downstream water users or the value of water use opportunities foreclosed by its effluent discharge. Under some circumstances there are economies of scale in waste disposal that cannot be realized by an individual firm or city acting independently.

Because of these features of waste disposal, market forces are supplemented in a variety of ways. Appeals are made to civic responsibility to minimize waste contribution to water courses. Damaged parties may resort to adversary proceedings in courts of law. Financial inducements to encourage waste treatment by municipalities are offered by the federal government, and storage to augment low flows is provided at federal expense. No doubt these practices have contributed a great deal toward reducing the offsite costs associated with waste disposal. But in the application of these practices there has not been a systematic balancing of costs and returns to achieve optimum benefits from the use of water resources including their use for waste disposal.

Water quality management raises three main issues: How do we determine the quality of water we want to maintain in our streams? How do we devise the best physical systems for achieving that quality? And how do we determine the best institutional arrangements for administering and managing water quality?

Before long, many streams will be free of the grossest and most obvious forms of pollution such as floating materials and suspended matter, since it is widely accepted that the social costs of permitting such pollution outweigh the social costs of removing it, at least in heavily populated areas. This type of pollution can be controlled in a comparatively efficient way by treatment at individual outfalls. Once this is done, we still face the question of what qualities of water are appropriate for the many uses of water courses? To what extent should we limit the use of streams for waste disposal now and in the future? How can we achieve a proper balance between this use and other valuable, and usually conflicting, uses such as municipal and industrial water supply and recreation? Removal of the most blatantly offensive material is but a beginning. It is one thing to remove fecal solids from a stream and another to assure that residual organic wastes do not interfere with fish culture by causing periodic deterioration of oxygen. It is one thing to remove oil from an industrial effluent and another to assure that residual phenols do not impose an increased treatment cost upon downstream municipal water users. We encounter a whole new array of pollutants which may have little effect on the appearance of the water but whose other effects can be costly and widespread. These pollutants can impose treatment costs on successive users, damage facilities of various kinds, make it necessary to turn to alternative sources of water, and reduce the value of water for recreation. Decisions must be made, for the conflicts between water uses are becoming stronger as economic development increases the demand on water courses. Recreational demand is growing at an especially rapid rate, outpacing the increase in population and in per capita income.

Once the floating and suspended materials have been removed from effluents, quality control moves beyond treatment in individual municipal and industrial plants, and can be managed in a number of ways. Because the level of streamflow affects water quality, it may be feasible to store water in large reservoirs during periods of high flow and release it during lower flows, or to temporarily store wastes and release them when flows are high. Measures can be taken to enhance the self-purification capacity of streams; and waste reclamation and process changes can reduce industrial waste loads. Even the location of economic activities becomes an important determinant of the cost of waste disposal and water supply facilities.

What is the ideal combination of alternatives? Or, to put it slightly differently, how can we determine the economically optimal regional system for managing water quality? This question increases in significance as the costs (abatement and damages) associated with waste disposal rise.

The importance of achieving efficient systems for water supply and waste disposal is emphasized by preliminary projections made for the Senate Select Committee.[1] While they must be interpreted cautiously, these projections indicate that many billions of dollars for public and private funds may be spent in the next couple of decades to control the quality of our water resources. Indeed, one might well hazard the guess that there will be a greater demand for expending public funds in water quality management than in any other area of resources development and use.

The third major issue involves the problem of devising appropriate institutional forms and tools of administration for management of water quality.

Recognition of the limitations of civic responsibility and of law and adversary proceedings in controlling the quality of our streams has caused us to go beyond them to administrative regulation of waste discharges from cities and industries, usually on the basis of some sort of general standards. In more recent years the federal government has provided financial assistance to local communities for the construction of waste treatment facilities. Also the federal government now provides low-flow augmentation on a non-reimbursable basis (provided certain standards of treatment are met) from federal multipurpose reservoirs. Are these the best methods for obtaining optimal management of the quality of water resources? Or should serious thought be given to revising the governmental structures and management tools now used in controlling water quality?

The objective of this book is to help shed light on these vital issues. The means used for this purpose are the economic theory of resources allocation and case studies of some actual situations. A central concern of economics has been the matter of allocating scarce resources to alternative ends. In ordinary instances the market may be

---

[1] *Water Resources Activities in the United States—Water Supply and Demand,* Select Committee on National Water Resources, United States Senate, Committee Print No. 32, by Nathaniel Wollman (Washington: U.S. Government Printing Office, August, 1960).

expected to perform this allocation in a reasonably satisfactory fashion. Because of the special circumstances [2] involved in the development and use of water resources, the market, as already implied, cannot be expected to allocate water efficiently or to generate efficient means of management. Economics, which has been called the "science of choice," can help to devise decision criteria which public or co-operative agencies can use in the management of water resources.

A certain amount of the special terminology which economists use in formulating and expressing their ideas is used in this study. The book is, however, not directed toward professional economists only, and an effort has been made to avoid technical language insofar as the subject matter will permit. Free use is made of appendices, and most of the more specialized economic materials are consigned to them.

The plan of the book falls into four sections. Part I consists of the introduction and chapter 2, which is directed toward readers without prior knowledge of some of the scientific and technological aspects of water quality. Chapter 2 identifies the major waste materials entering watercourses and their effects on the receiving water, outlines the effects of these materials on water uses, and sketches some of the more important methods of treating both water supplies and waste waters. It also discusses other quality control measures which may be substituted for treatment at least over certain ranges.

Part II, consisting of chapters 3, 4, and 5, outlines the economic resources allocation theory as it relates specifically to waste disposal problems. The major focus is upon the problems presented by the "offsite" costs imposed upon subsequent users when wastes are discharged into watercourses.

Water pollution is a traditional example that economists have used to illustrate what are formidably called "technological external diseconomies." This expression, to simplify greatly, means certain inefficiencies that occur because some costs can be shifted from one independent economic unit to another. Chapter 3 endeavors to explain this concept and relate it specifically to the problem of appropriate policy to redress cost distortions resulting from waste disposal.

[2] These "circumstances" are external economies and diseconomies, economies of large scale, and collective good aspects. Each of these concepts is explained in some detail in following chapters.

Chapter 4 deals with problems in assessing the value of offsite costs of waste disposal and procedures for dealing with situations where not all values can be assessed in a commensurable way.

Chapter 5 is designed to lend concreteness to many of the points discussed in a hypothetical context in chapters 3 and 4. Here, the suggested criteria of cost assessment and redistribution are applied to a water quality problem in the Ohio Basin.

Part III deals with regional waste disposal systems. Because there are substantial economies of scale in certain means of abatement, it is necessary to consider some alternatives that cannot be efficiently utilized by the individual (municipal or industrial) waste discharger. Efficient waste disposal on a regional basis demands that a system incorporating the available scale economies be designed and operated through some sort of co-operative arrangement or by a public authority. Chapter 6 deals with design and operation criteria for an economically optimal system of regional waste disposal. Consideration is given to the many devices for managing water quality that may be available in any given region. These include, in addition to waste treatment and the regulation of streamflows, product and process adjustment by industry, temporary storage of wastes during periods of low streamflow, artificial reaeration of streams, and in specific instances others as well. It is explained that a water quality control system is part of general water resources management and must be planned and operated in full cognizance of its competitive and complementary relationships with the over-all water management system. In addition, procedures are discussed for incorporating in the design procedures those values which cannot be, or are not, made commensurable with others. The design problem is also related to the probability characteristic of costs, which results from variations in streamflow.

Chapter 7 relates the economic principles discussed in this study to the operation of regional waste disposal systems in the Ruhr industrial area of West Germany. The German water associations are the only organizations in the world which have designed, built, and operated regional systems of waste disposal and have developed comparatively sophisticated methods of assessing costs and levying charges on effluents.

The final chapter summarizes the general conclusions and discusses their implications for present and future policy. Attention is also given to the institutional arrangements needed for the implementation and administration of efficient waste disposal systems.

2

Some Technical and Engineering
Facts Concerning Water Quality

~~~~~~

Water pollution results from a great variety of causes, produces complex changes in receiving waters, and affects subsequent water uses in numerous, rather subtle, as well as obvious, ways. A full description of the physical aspects of water pollution and the technical devices available for its abatement can easily fill an extensive volume. The discussion in this chapter is but a brief introduction to these matters, designed as a background for consideration of the economics of water quality management.[1]

MAJOR TYPES OF POLLUTANTS
AND THEIR EFFECTS ON RECEIVING WATERS

Degradable and Non-degradable Pollutants

The many impurities that enter watercourses as a result of man's domestic, industrial, and agricultural activities can be grouped in a variety of ways depending upon the purpose of the classification. One very broad division, which emphasizes occurrences within the receiv-

---

[1] Citations and specific examples are provided in this chapter only for new or comparatively rarely used devices or procedures which are not, or not adequately, covered in the standard references. Where no specific citation is given, the reader who wishes to obtain detailed information can turn to any one of several thorough discussions of the technological aspects of waste water disposal and water supply. Good examples are Gordon Maskew Fair and John Charles Geyer, *Water Supply and Waste Water Disposal* (New York: John Wiley & Sons, 1956), and Louis Klein, *Aspects of River Pollution* (New York: Academic Press, Inc., 1957).

ing water, distinguishes between degradable and non-degradable pollutants.

Non-degradable pollutants are not altered by the biological processes that occur in natural waters. For the most part, they are the inorganic chemicals such as chlorides which are diluted by the receiving water, but not appreciably reduced in quantity. The sources of these pollutants are many and widespread. Industrial wastes frequently contain numerous such pollutants in the form of metallic salts and other toxic, corrosive, colored, and taste-producing materials; domestic water use modestly raises the content of chlorides and other dissolved salts; irrigation may result in a highly saline return flow; and troublesome concentrations of chlorides frequently arise from natural sources. In heavily industrialized areas and in the irrigated areas of the West, these pollutants are frequently the most troublesome of all.

Classified as non-degradable for practical purposes are radiological waste products and the persistent organics. Radioactive elements do decay, but the process can be extremely slow. The persistent organics, which include many of the organic compounds synthesized by the chemical industry, are not strictly non-degradable, but they resist attack by stream biota. They are also resistant to treatment, since typical waste treatment utilizes biota found in streams. Some of the organic chemicals found in streams are comparatively common ones such as DDT, 2,4-D, chlordane, cyanides, and synthetic detergents. These and many other complex industrial, agricultural, and pharmaceutical chemicals all offer difficult treatment problems. The agricultural chemicals present a special problem as they are delivered to streams in storm runoff from the land and bypass waste treatment plants.

Suspended materials create special problems which are of major significance in some basins. These pollutants include the silt and other suspended sediment from land erosion and dredging, and the colloidal matter from domestic and industrial waste and from deposits of clay particles. These are non-degradable pollutants in the sense that they are not changed in form. The silt and other suspended sediment usually settles out, especially in slow stretches of stream or in impoundments, but the colloidal matter remains. Both types of matter create turbidity. Not only does turbidity make the water unattractive, but it can be damaging to fish, and it inhibits algae growth, which depends upon light. The latter may be favorable or unfavorable depending on the circumstances.

Degradable wastes are the substances that are changed in form and/or reduced in quantity by the biological, chemical, and physical phenomena characteristic of natural waters. By far the most widespread, though not the greatest, source of such materials is domestic sewage. This highly unstable, putrescible, organic waste can be converted to stable inorganic materials (bicarbonates, nitrates, sulfates, and phosphates) by the bacteria and other organisms found in natural water bodies. If water is not too heavily loaded, this process, which is commonly but somewhat deceptively known as self-purification, will proceed aerobically (by the action of bacteria utilizing free oxygen) and will not produce offensive odors. If, however, the receiving waters are loaded beyond a certain level, the process of degradation becomes anaerobic (proceeds by the action of bacteria not utilizing free oxygen), and noxious hydrogen sulfide, and other gases are produced.

The processes—aerobic and anaerobic—which naturally occur in streams are utilized in sewage treatment plants, and indeed are the major elements in ordinary domestic sewage treatment. In essence, treatment plants systematize, control, and accelerate the processes which would have occurred in any case and, by doing so, can limit the self-purification burden put upon a water body.

The most recent estimate of total organic waste loads discharged into watercourses from industries and municipalities indicates that in 1960 municipal effluents accounted for about 75 million population equivalents, while industrial discharges contained about 150 million population equivalents.[2] The population equivalent is a measure which standardizes oxygen-demanding wastes on the basis of the oxygen demand of untreated wastes stemming from one person. The food, pulp and paper, chemical, and petroleum-refining industries are the largest producers of organic wastes.

Bacterial pollution has been a major focus of pollution control policy, and the coliform count has been developed as an index of sewage pollution. The real sources of concern are the bacteria that cause infectious diseases, primarily typhoid, dysentery, and cholera.

[2] See Murray Stein, "Problems and Programs in Water Pollution," *Natural Resources Journal*, December, 1962, p. 398.

These may be considered degradable pollutants since they tend to die off rather quickly after leaving the body, and a stream is usually capable of purifying itself of these bacteria during the course of its flow. Where treatment is required, disinfection with chlorine has proved highly effective.

The presence of viruses in sewage and in watercourses has recently drawn much attention. Viruses present a greater control problem as they are much more resistant to disinfectants than pathogenic bacteria and can exist in a dormant condition outside living organisms.

BOD, the Oxygen Sag, and Algae

Given an amount of discharge, it is not particularly difficult to predict the concentration of non-degradable pollutants in receiving waters, since dilution is essentially the only process involved if the pollutant is in solution. However, predicting the level of unassimilated, degradable organic wastes, the rate of waste degradation, and important associated variables, presents more difficult technical problems.

A measure of organic pollution load is biochemical oxygen demand (BOD), which indicates the rate at which dissolved oxygen is drawn upon in a stream. The rate at which a given quantity and type of organic waste exerts oxygen demand is a function of a variety of factors, among the most important of which are the chemical characteristics and temperature of the receiving water. Toxins, for example, may appreciably reduce the rate of BOD by inhibiting bacterial action. In extreme instances of toxic pollution, a body of water may become bacteriologically "dead." At higher temperatures bacterial action is accelerated, wastes are degraded more rapidly, and dissolved oxygen in the water is drawn upon more heavily. Since the oxygen saturation level of warm water is lower than that of cooler water, higher temperatures tend to squeeze dissolved oxygen levels in waste-receiving waters, and septic (anaerobic) conditions may result. It is for this reason—as well as typically low streamflows—that summer is usually the critical period for organic pollution.

The rate of BOD combined with the rate at which oxygen is restored determines the level of dissolved oxygen. In flowing water the combined effect of BOD and reaeration results first in a fall and then a rise in dissolved oxygen as the wastes are carried downstream. This phenomenon is described by a characteristic curve known as the oxygen sag. The low, or critical, point on the oxygen sag is a governing factor in the design of sewage treatment plants. Sanitary engineering practice has typically been to calculate the oxygen sag at a given (low) level of streamflow and to design a waste water treatment plant capable of yielding a specified level of dissolved oxygen at the low point of the oxygen sag. A pair of dissolved oxygen sags resulting from a single waste outfall is shown schematically in Figure 1. Other things being equal, factors that reduce the rate of BOD lengthen and

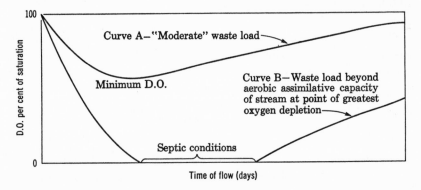

Figure 1. Schematic primary oxygen sag assuming that waste enters a clean stream fully saturated with dissolved oxygen.

flatten the oxygen sag, while those that accelerate BOD have the reverse effect. The shape of the oxygen sag is also affected by the rate of reaeration (which depends largely on turbulence, the area of the air-water interface, and photosynthetic oxygen production) and by the velocity of streamflow.

Consideration of waste disposal problems on a regional basis requires a method of tracing the effects of wastes on long stretches of stream. Where wastes enter streams at closely spaced waste outfalls, the level of dissolved oxygen at any given point will be a function of the rate of reaeration and the exertion of BOD from numerous different sources. At a downstream point the BOD from the more distant sources may be almost exhausted while that from nearer sources will still be exerted at a high rate. A D.O. (dissolved oxygen) profile for a long stretch of such a stream will show deep valleys below large outfalls or closely spaced small outfalls and perhaps nearly saturation level at other points. Figure 2 shows an oxygen profile of the Ohio River obtained by computer simulation for given conditions of flow, temperature and waste load. Procedures are being developed for forecasting regional oxygen profiles under differing conditions of

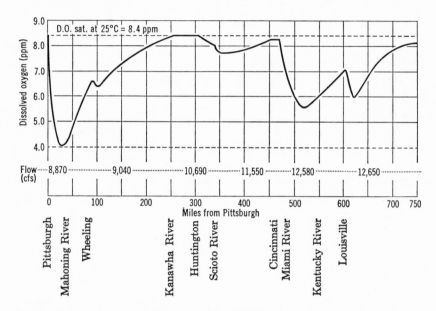

Figure 2. Dissolved oxygen profile projected for the Ohio River for 1980 on the assumption of medium growth, 70% treatment, temperature of 25°C., K_2 (reoxygenation-rate coefficient) = 0.1, and K_1 (deoxygenation coefficient) = 0.435.
(*Source:* R. L. O'Connell, *et al., op. cit.,* fn. 3.)

streamflow, water temperature, and other relevant variables. These involve mathematically simulating the behavior of the wastes and the stream, usually on a computer.[3] These procedures are still far from

[3] See R. L. O'Connell, J. B. Cohen, E. C. Tzivoglou, "Future Stream Flow Requirements for Organic Pollution Abatement, Ohio River Basin," U.S. Public Health Service, Robert A. Taft Sanitary Engineering Center, Cincinnati, mimeo. See also *"Oxsag," A Program for Analyzing the Biological Quality of Water in a Flowing Stream by Means of the Oxygen Sag Curve Equation,* Prepared for U.S. Public Health Service, Region VII, Dallas, by Freese, Nichols and Endress, Consulting Engineers, Fort Worth, Texas, January, 1961. Bauassessor Dr. Boehnke of the Emschergenossenschaft (Emscher River Association) in West Germany is

comprehending the complexity of events in a stream, but they are very promising.

Among the complexities that beset the calculation of oxygen levels, especially for long stretches of stream, is the fact that BOD proceeds in two stages. When an untreated waste is put in a clean stream a first, and major, draft upon dissolved oxygen occurs as the putrescible wastes are degraded by bacterial action. Thereafter the dissolved oxygen level tends to recover. Further downstream, roughly five to seven days' travel time, a "second stage" BOD occurs as the nitrogen embodied in the organic waste is converted to nitrite and then to nitrate by aerobic nitrifying bacteria. The second stage BOD is more diffuse and does not by itself tend to carry D.O. to as low a level as does the first stage BOD.

Both the degradation of putrescible wastes and the process of nitrification can be carried on in a treatment plant as well as in the receiving water. Indeed, the former is the primary function of orthodox biological treatment plants. However, orthodox treatment measures do not fully complete either process; the water's self-purification capacity is always called upon to a degree. Since the effectiveness of BOD removal declines as the per cent removed increases, treatment becomes more and more expensive as it proceeds to higher levels, and removal of the last few per cent becomes extremely costly.

The residual products of organic waste degradation are plant nutrients—nitrogen, phosphorous, carbon. Under propitious conditions of temperature and water clarity, these give rise to algae growth which in turn affects the oxygen balance in the receiving water. Since algae produce organic matter by means of photosynthesis, they at least

---

preparing a program for quickly and flexibly forecasting oxygen conditions throughout the length of the Lippe River under varying conditions of flow, temperature, etc. The Battelle-Institut, Frankfurt/Main, is working on an analogous procedure. See "Kurzberichte der Wasserwirtschaft," *Die Wasserwirtschaft,* February, 1962, p. 56. Work on procedures to simulate the behavior of wastes in long stretches of stream is also under way in the Department of Engineering and Applied Physics at Harvard University under the direction of Harold Thomas. See Harold A. Thomas, Jr., and Robert P. Burden, *Operations Research in Water Quality Management,* Harvard Water Resources Group, Final Report to Division of Water Supply and Pollution Control, U.S. Public Health Service, Chapter 3, "Queuing Model for Pollution Transport in Streams."

periodically release oxygen. And, mass deaths of algae, such as may occur in cold weather or after several days of cloudy weather, put a sudden heavy BOD load upon the water.[4] If algae are present in great quantities, they affect the appearance, taste, and odor of water.

Automatic Monitoring of Stream and Effluent Quality

The past several years have seen considerable advances in the development of devices that can qualitatively and quantitatively analyze residual waste materials in watercourses. In many cases these are comparatively simple electrical devices. In a few locations such variables of river quality as dissolved oxygen, acidity, alkalinity, salinity, specific conductance (dissolved solids), temperature, and turbidity are continuously measured with a reasonable degree of accuracy. While continuous measurement of a number of important quality parameters still presents serious problems, and the monitoring of effluents presents its own set of difficulties, rapid development is taking place.[5]

Concluding Comments

While a simple classification system is a convenient point of departure, it must inevitably obscure the highly complex phenomena that occur in a stream. A vast number of substances enter watercourses. Some result from man's activities and others are of natural origin, and their effects are interrelated in a variety of complicated ways.

Lakes, reservoirs, and tidal estuaries present even more difficult problems for analysis than flowing streams. Deposition of sludge banks, with the possibility of their sudden dispersal resulting in a pollution "shock load," is one complication characteristic of quiescent waters. Stratification—the formation of thermal layers which prevent deep circulation—is another difficulty besetting analysis of lakes and reser-

[4] For a simplified discussion of some important unsolved problems with respect to algae growth and decay and its effects on dissolved oxygen, see Allen V. Kneese, *Water Pollution: Economic Aspects and Research Needs* (Washington, D.C.: Resources for the Future, Inc., 1962), p. 51.

[5] For a discussion of the possible role of automatic monitoring procedures in the economics of water quality management and citations to the literature, see p. 70, chapter 4.

voirs. Plant nutrients also take on special significance in these bodies of water because they tend to accumulate over time and contribute to depletion of oxygen at lower levels. In tidal estuaries wastes may be carried back and forth within the estuary for long periods of time rather than disperse into the ocean. Thus unassimilated or partially assimilated wastes may build up in estuarine areas and become particularly troublesome.

Much has been done to develop generalizations about the receiving water environment and to apply scientific principles to it. However, precision is less and uncertainty greater in this area than in most fields of scientific and engineering forecasting. This emphasizes the importance of empirical checking of forecasts made upon the basis of highly simplified principles.

EFFECTS OF POLLUTION ON WATER USES

Aesthetic and Recreational Considerations

The earliest efforts to control pollution had their origin in man's aesthetic sensitivities. The repulsive suffocating reek of large cities of early modern times is made plain in many accounts. The smells so graphically described were largely the result of the anaerobic processes mentioned earlier. Nuisance odors can be eliminated by satisfactorily designed sewers that convey wastes to an adequate supply of dilution water, but the early sewers often served merely to concentrate the odor-producing processes in the neighborhood of outfalls.

Odors are not the only offensive aspect of polluted water. Floating materials of many kinds are likely to be unsightly and floating sewage solids especially so. Turbid or highly colored waters resulting from silt or industrial wastes, including dyes, reduce the visual appeal of water, as do the dense algae growths that flourish where there are large supplies of sewage residual plant nutrients.

The rewards of water-based recreation are certainly related to the aesthetic qualities of water, but the recreational value of water can be reduced or eliminated by pollution which does not render the water repulsive or even necessarily unattractive. For example, the organic waste load in a stream may reduce D.O. levels to a point where the best quality fish are unable to survive, or toxins from industrial plants or agricultural lands may kill fish directly, interfere with a phase of their life cycle, or affect a necessary food source. Higher temperatures, excessive acidity or alkalinity, and low D.O., all of which can result from man-made pollution, increase the sensitivity of fish to toxins and in extreme instances can themselves kill fish. On the other hand, a modest degree of sewage pollution can benefit fishing waters by promoting increased algae growth, which enters into the food chain. Extensive growths, however, can be toxic to fish. A special problem occurs in reservoirs where algae growth and decay combined with absence of deep circulation cause the deeper parts to become devoid of dissolved oxygen and, consequently, uninhabitable for fish.

The effect of pollution on bathing also extends beyond aesthetic considerations. Water may look attractive but be deemed unsafe for swimming because of its bacteria content.

Domestic Supplies

The amount and character of treatment required for domestic water supplies is related to the quality of intake water. When water contains organic substances that are only partly assimilated, it must be treated with larger amounts of chlorine to kill bacteria. When it is corrosive, saline, or hard, public supplies may require special treatment, and costs to water users are increased by the need for special equipment, larger quantities of soap, and purchases of bottled water.

Furthermore, water is made less palatable by certain pollutants. Algae may cause unattractive tastes and odors, and when present in large amounts they increase treatment problems. A great variety of chemicals of industrial origin affect the palatability and possibly the safety of water supplies and consequently may require special treatment; in some cases they may even make a water supply completely unsuitable for domestic use. The appearance of water is also affected by industrial and domestic pollution. The appeal of drinking water, for example, is reduced by color, or by the foaming which results from even minute concentrations of detergents.

Industrial Supplies

Many industrial processes utilize a quality of water not unlike that usually prepared by municipal treatment plants. However, the range of qualities required or desirable in industrial application is very wide. Cooling water can often be of comparatively low sanitary quality, but heat and corrosive and scale-forming materials are undesirable. In terms of over-all quantities of water involved, cooling is by far the most important industrial use. Some 80 per cent of industrial use is for this purpose.

Generally speaking, process uses are considerably more sensitive to water quality. Some processes require unusually soft water, while others need comparatively hard water. A large part of the water used in the paper and pulp industry can be of relatively poor quality in some respects, but it should be low in iron, manganese, and carbon dioxide. High-pressure boiler feed water, used in a variety of industries, must be of high quality primarily to prevent corrosion and scale formation. Steel rolling mills are damaged by water containing concentrations of chlorides tolerable in drinking water.

METHODS OF TREATMENT

In general, the quality of water bodies can be improved either by treating entering wastes or by increasing dilution. As long as dilution water can be made available and the focus is upon maintenance of quality during low-flow periods, treatment and dilution are technical substitutes, except to the degree that floating materials may cause aesthetic nuisance. Increased dilution can be attained by altering the time pattern of streamflows, by altering the time pattern of waste discharge, or by doing both simultaneously. Given the degree of dilution, water supply treatment can be a partial substitute for sewage treatment. Indeed if water were not useful, offensive, or altered in quality while *in situ*, water supply treatment would be technically interchangeable with sewage treatment.

Process changes in industry which recover, reclaim, or otherwise reduce waste loads, as well as disposal of waste waters on the land, are within limits alternatives to treatment.

A water utilization system in a region (say a river basin) could be designed to incorporate a variety of measures including water supply treatment, sewage treatment, augmented dilution flows, process changes, co-ordination of effluent releases with river flow, disposal of waste on the land, and perhaps others. The economic considerations concerning the elements to be included in ideal, or optimal, systems are discussed later. The next few pages present a very brief outline of the general character of the major available control measures. A primary point to be made is that the limit upon society's ability to avoid water pollution is not technical but economic. Technological means are currently available to purify water to any desired degree.

Treatment of Waste Water

It is possible to obtain completely pure water from sewage effluent by a series of treatment steps, which might include distillation or other measures to remove dissolved solids such as ion exchange, electrodialysis, and semipermeable membrane techniques. At the present time, however, orthodox treatment of domestic wastes is a comparatively standardized process that can greatly reduce but not eliminate BOD and that is frequently designed to improve bacteriological quality. Industrial waste treatment is generally similar, but it sometimes includes techniques for treating color, neutralizing acidity or alkalinity, or reducing the concentration of various chemicals (primarily by precipitation or ion exchange).

Ordinarily the treatment of degradable organic wastes begins with removal of the larger solids by screening and the more finely divided ones by sedimentation. This stage, known as primary treatment, produces a wet, difficult-to-handle sludge, which is usually digested in heated anaerobic tanks before final disposal. In some cases, the sludge is burned after partial or complete drying, and recently the burning of wet sludge has attracted attention. Primary treatment, with sludge disposal, of an effluent containing organic wastes reduces the first stage BOD by perhaps 40 per cent.

A secondary stage of treatment is biological in character and essentially controls and accelerates the self-purification processes of natural waters. Two major techniques are presently used. In the trickling filter method, a biological film is grown on rocks or plastic media, and the waste is sprayed intermittently, allowing air contact with at least the surface of the film. In the activated sludge technique, air or oxygen is forced into a tank containing a mix of waste and actively feeding biota. Part of the settled sludge containing the biota is recirculated and mixed with wastes in the aeration chamber. Each of these methods has certain advantages. Trickling filters require relatively little attention during operation, and the biological growths upon which their effectiveness depends are somewhat less susceptible to toxins. The activated sludge plant is somewhat more flexible in operation and design; the major variables are generally the proportion of sludge recirculated, length of aerating time, and amount of air introduced. Rapid turnover of waste and sludge generally saves space and power, but requires well-trained operating personnel. Small package plants called extended aeration plants have had considerable success in handling a slow turnover. These plants are easy to operate, the sludge withdrawals are small enough to be discharged with the effluent, and much more of the solid matter is in mineralized form. Treatment can be made more effective by increasing the amount of air passed through the activated sludge tank, but costs mount rapidly as BOD removal is pushed above, say, 95 per cent.

When secondary treatment is undertaken the supernatant liquor from the sludge digestor, or other liquid resulting from the handling of sludge, is routed through the secondary treatment process. Secondary treatment in turn gives rise to some additional sludge which is routed into the digestors.

Primary and secondary treatment combined usually reduces BOD by some 85 to 95 per cent. The procedures outlined above, plus chlorination in some instances, have been the essential elements of the primary/secondary treatment sequence for more than forty years.

During secondary treatment the nitrogen content of the sewage is successively converted to nitrites and nitrates. Over all, the volume of potential plant nutrients (nitrogen and phosphorous) is reduced modestly during secondary treatment, but the content of nitrogen in nitrate form, of course, rises. Within limits, the extent to which nitrification occurs in the treatment plant, rather than in the receiving water, can be controlled.

When effluent of a particularly high quality is desired, or an unusually difficult treatment problem exists, the components or combinations of components in the treatment sequence may be altered. Chemical treatment is sometimes used to deal with seasonal or other specialized treatment problems. For example, by means of precipitation and flocculation much of the suspended matter (not subject to ordinary sedimentation) and some dissolved solids can be settled out of water containing organic wastes. There is presently considerable interest in the use of chemicals in sewage treatment both as a separate method and as a means of increasing the effect of other treatment methods during critical periods. Some laboratory experiments have shown a reduction of 60 to 85 per cent in BOD without biological treatment.[6] While chemical treatment is expensive during the time it is in operation, it may have an economic comparative advantage over more capital-intensive means for dealing with pollution levels that are reached only infrequently.[7]

A device sometimes used to improve final effluent is a finishing pond. This is an aerobic lagoon in which biological processes are permitted to continue before the effluent is finally expelled into the receiving water.

Similar types of ponds are increasingly used, either as complete or as secondary treatment devices, especially in smaller communities and in industry. Algae play an important role in the oxidation ponds. They furnish, by means of photosynthesis, a substantial share of the oxygen requirements of aerobic bacteria, and they utilize the gases from the anaerobic BOD removal in bottom sludge banks and reduce or prevent their escape to the atmosphere. Such ponds, when properly designed and loaded, are capable of stabilizing oxygen-demanding wastes to a high degree. Similar effects result from the extended aeration plant,

[6] See "Polymer Speeds Sewage Treatment," *Engineering News Record*, March 29, 1962, p. 49.
[7] This point is elaborated in chapter 6.

which is also primarily suitable for smaller communities. In this type of plant, the sludge is digested in the same unit where biological treatment occurs, and mineralized to a far-reaching extent. Both the oxidation pond and the extended aeration plant differ from standard treatment in that their effluents contain virtually *all* the plant nutrients originally in the sewage; in the former case, they are largely embodied in algae, in the latter, in mineral form. Thus the effluents from oxidation ponds and extended aeration plants fertilize a stream more than do those from orthodox plants.[8]

In the Ruhr industrial area of West Germany comparatively large shallow impoundments have been constructed in several rivers to serve essentially as large oxidation ponds in the stream itself. One of them is designed to neutralize acids and to precipitate organic materials simultaneously. This is possible because of the specific types of wastes which are delivered into it.[9]

If fish or algae were harvested from oxidation ponds,[10] the process of biological purification would be accelerated and a major portion of the plant nutrients, as well as some other chemicals would be extracted from the waste water. High-rate oxidation ponds and related "tertiary" treatment methods for plant nutrients are presently in an experimental stage.

Recently the U.S. Public Health Service has undertaken a substantial effort to develop treatment methods to remove presently difficult-to-handle substances, like plant nutrients, from water and waste water.[11]

[8] A review of U.S. and European experience with extended aeration plants (called *Totalklaeranlagen* in Germany) can be found in D. Kehr, "Die Technischen Moeglichkeiten der Abwasserbehandlung in Kleinen Gemeinden" (Technical Possibilities for Handling Effluents in Small Communities) read before a meeting Abwasserbehandlung in kleinen und mittleren Gemeinden, Haus der Technik, Essen, May 11, 1962.

The literature on stabilization ponds is by now quite extensive. A general discussion is W. W. Towne and W. H. Davis, "Sewage Treatment by Raw Stabilization Ponds," *Journal of Sanitary Engineering Division—Proceedings of the American Society of Civil Engineers,* August, 1957.

[9] The system of lagoons in the Ruhr is described further in chapter 7, fn. 6.

[10] At the present time fish are harvested in a few locations in Europe and Asia. Algae have been harvested only on an experimental basis.

[11] See *Advanced Waste Treatment Research,* 1 and 2, U.S. Public Health Service, Robert A. Taft Sanitary Engineering Center, Cincinnati, May, 1962, and September, 1962.

Water Supply Treatment

Essentially the same principles apply to water supply and waste water treatment. Technically, the steps usually associated with waste water treatment could be combined with others and performed at the water treatment plant. In the few instances where sewage effluent has been recirculated for potable supply, water treatment was essentially an extension of sewage treatment. In practice, however, treatment of water from a surface source often begins with coagulation and sedimentation, followed by filtration through sand to clarify the water and reduce the number of bacteria. Groundwater is often treated to remove iron and manganese. Sometimes water is softened, and it is treated, at least periodically, with lime to reduce corrosiveness. Activated carbon may be used when the water contains persistent organics.[12] Finally, chlorine is usually added to the water to destroy harmful organisms. The amount required is, among other things, a function of the unassimilated organic wastes in the water.

Industrial water supply treatment typically includes some or all of the same steps. Quality requirements vary widely, however, and large amounts of industrial water can be treated by other methods as well as those suitable for potable supplies. Manufacturers may harden or soften water, adjust its alkalinity or acidity, and remove undesirable chemical substances of various kinds. In uses where extremely high quality is critical, water may even be demineralized or distilled prior to use.

Direct Recirculation, Desalinization,
Divided Distribution Systems, and Artificial Recharge

Treated municipal sewage has been recirculated for public water supplies only in conditions of extreme stringency. The most widely known instance of recirculation in the United States occurred in Chanute, Kansas, during the winter of 1956–57. Sewage was also reused for all municipal purposes by Lyndon, Kansas, in the fall of

---

[12] The use of activated carbon adds greatly to the cost of water supply treatment.

1956, when the normal water supply was exhausted. Ottumwa, Iowa, faced what amounted to a reuse problem in some respects more difficult than that of the other cities, when about 60 per cent of the flow in the Des Moines River, the supply source, consisted of septic raw sewage, discharged by the City of Des Moines.[13] There are, however, always alternative sources of supply—underground water and transportation of water from other locations, for example—although on occasion tapping them may involve rather extreme costs. This is an area where aesthetics are heavily involved, and society has usually preferred to avoid direct recirculation and turn to alternative sources of supply regardless of cost. Under some circumstances, however, recirculation might present an economical alternative to the usual practices.

To permit continuous recirculation for potable supply, current standard sewage and water treatment processes would have to be supplemented. Among the most difficult problems to deal with is the buildup of dissolved solids. However, treatment processes could be devised which would continuously produce potable water supplies from sewage at lesser costs than would be involved in, say, the conversion of sea water or the treatment of water from a stream highly polluted with certain industrial wastes. Partial recirculation could help ease the burden on treatment facilities, as some effluent might be continuously discharged and replaced with fresh makeup water. Direct reuse of treated sewage effluent for certain industrial purposes is not only technically possible but is practiced on a rather large scale. The most widely known instance is the use of treated sewage from the city of Baltimore by a steel plant at Sparrows Point. However, there are numerous additional instances, especially in the western United States.[14]

A separate distribution system for potable supplies has often been proposed. With respect to recirculation this might mean that a com-

[13] See Bernard B. Berger, "Public Health Aspects of Water Reuse for Potable Supply," *Journal American Water Works Association,* Vol. 52, No. 5, May, 1960, pp. 599ff. In the special circumstances of cities which otherwise discharge effluents into the ocean or other places from which they cannot be reclaimed, recirculation would constitute a net saving of water.

[14] See Select Committee on National Water Resources, United States Senate, Committee Print No. 30, *Present and Prospective Means for Improved Reuse of Water* (Washington: U.S. Government Printing Office, 1960).

paratively small proportion of the water supply would be highly treated, perhaps distilled for drinking water, while the remainder would be recirculated with less extensive treatment for general municipal and industrial use. Alternatively, a fresh supply (presumably limited in amount or expensive to tap) could be used for potable supplies, while the treated effluent is recirculated for general municipal uses. The fresh potable supply could serve as makeup water to prevent the buildup of dissolved solids in the recirculated portion. Another alternative is a separate circulation system for potable supplies. Public health authorities have generally been critical of plans of this character because of the dangers involved in accidental cross connections or deliberate use of the non-potable supplies for human ingestion. However, a separated system (for industrial supplies) exists in Krefeld in the Ruhr area and will in the course of time be extended through much of the Ruhr industrial region.[15] There are also examples of less extensive dual systems in the United States.

Groundwater recharge is a possible alternative way of making treated sewage or heavily used river waters available for general reuse. This can be accomplished by means of injection wells or spreading grounds. With the spreading technique, the water undergoes additional purification as it passes through the unsaturated zone. The purification process in the soil results from the action of soil bacteria, filtration, adsorption, and perhaps other processes.[16] However, the minerals remain, and the salinity buildup limits reuse.

Caution in the use of reclaimed sewage for recharge is in order because groundwater contamination tends to be persistent, and a sig-

---

[15] For a description of the dual system of treatment and distribution in Krefeld, see Walter Herrman and Walter Czerwenkz, "Aufbereitung und Schoenung des Rheinwassers in Krefeld" (Preparation and Improvement of Rhein Water in Krefeld), *Wasser-Abwasser*, Heft 14, 1 April, 1960.

[16] Recharge of groundwater supplies for municipal use has been used in the Ruhr area of Germany for many years. The recharge water is obtained from the heavily used rivers, and recharge is accomplished in such a way that the water filters through the ground. For a brief description of this procedure see *Gelsenwasser— Herausgegeben anlaesslich des 75 jaehrigen Bestehens des Wasserwerk fuer das noerdliche Westfaelische Kohlenrevier, Gelsenkirchen*, Gelsenkirchen, January, 1962. Closer to home, Peoria, Illinois, provides an example of recharge from a river, the Illinois, whose quality is substantially lowered by discharges into it. See also Thomas W. Bendixson, Gordon G. Robeck, and Richard L. Woodward, "The Use of Soil for Liquid Waste Disposal and Treatment," U.S. Public Health Service, Robert A. Taft Sanitary Engineering Center, Cincinnati, March, 1963.

nificant amount of groundwater is used directly for potable supplies without previous treatment. The problems of groundwater contamination have recently been highlighted by the widespread discovery of ABS (alkyl benzene sulfonate) in well waters. The presence of ABS, which is the active ingredient in most household washing preparations, is largely attributable to the use of septic tanks in housing developments.[17]

Dilution

Because of the inverse relationship between the concentration of most pollutants and low-flow stages of streams, fuller use of higher streamflows suggests itself as a possibility. Low flows ordinarily coincide with a heavy concentration of pollutants, as well as with high temperatures, which depress the oxygen saturation level of receiving waters and increase the susceptibility of fish to toxins. The periods of low flow and potentially high pollution damage are, as indicated earlier, also the periods for which effluent treatment plants are designed.

Dilution of wastes beyond that provided by natural flow during low-flow periods can be provided by altering either the pattern of streamflow or the pattern of waste discharge. The usual practices are to augment low flows by controlled release from reservoir storage, and to adjust waste discharge by temporary storage of wastes. The temporary shutdown of polluting industrial plants during low stream stages is another alternative.

Dilution by flow augmentation or co-ordinated release is feasible for streams but not for lakes, and only to a limited extent for estuaries. Flow augmentation could actually increase pollution in lakes and estuaries by carrying greater quantities of partially assimilated wastes into these water bodies.

The augmentation of low streamflows may play a large role in future pollution abatement in the United States. Large-scale planning efforts by the U.S. Corps of Engineers in several eastern basins will

[17] Graham Walton, "ABS Contamination of Water Resources," *Journal American Water Works Association*, Vol. 52, No. 11, November, 1960.

apparently result in recommendations for large amounts of storage for the augmentation of flows.[18]

Some of the effects of storage on water quality are generally favorable and add to the advantage of flow augmentation in contrast to other measures. For example, the chemical and bacteriological quality of water is stabilized, and summer releases from reservoirs tend to be cooler than regular streamflow. On the other hand, some early hopes for effective dilution through flow augmentation were disappointed because of failure to consider the impact of impoundment upon the dissolved oxygen content of water. Water from deeper parts of reservoirs is often virtually devoid of oxygen, owing to the combined effect of BOD and reservoir stratification. This condition is particularly characteristic of areas experiencing hot summer seasons. Thus to achieve a given effect on downstream D.O., larger releases from the reservoir are required and the costs of achieving abatement via dilution are raised. However, methods of coping with this problem have been devised. For example, air has been successfully introduced into water passing through power turbines. In many installations this can be done comparatively simply by making use of "vacuum breakers" already installed in the dam. Turbine aeration involves some power loss, however, and therefore is not costless.[19]

Other methods of reaerating water or preventing reservoir stratification include high or multi-level penstock intakes, special tailrace design, compressed air reaeration, and circulation by pumping. The theoretical energy requirement for mixing reservoir water is quite small because of the modest net lift required.

The operation of reservoirs does not necessarily have a favorable effect on the assimilative capacity of streams even when viewed solely

[18] See Eugene Weber, "Relation of Regulation for Quality to Activities of the Corps of Engineers," *Symposium on Stream Flow Regulation for Water Quality Control* (mimeo.), Robert A. Taft Sanitary Engineering Center, Cincinnati, April 3, 1963.

[19] Turbine aeration has been used both here and in Europe. A. J. Wiley and B. F. Lueck and R. H. Scott and T. F. Wisniewski, "Commercial Scale Operation of Turbine Aeration on Wisconsin Rivers," *Journal Water Pollution Federation*, February, 1960. The most definitive German source is Hubert Wagner, *Die kuenstliche Belueftung kanalisierter Fluesse* (The Artificial Reaeration of Canalized Streams), Herausgegeben von der Bundesanstalt fuer Gewaesserkunde in Koblenz, 1956.

with respect to the volume of streamflow or dilution capacity. The use of power dams for "peaking" can result in a streamflow less favorable to waste disposal than the natural flow because surges of released water alternate with periods in which no releases are made. In these instances, changes in operating procedure or reregulation by means of small control structures downstream could cancel the unfavorable effects.

An alternative method of utilizing the dilution potentialities of streamflow is to withhold wastes in small impoundments and release them during periods of high streamflow. This temporary lagooning requires far less storage than impounding water upstream for dilution, but the space required is likely to be more costly. Also, temporary lagooning will reduce streamflow during low-flow periods. In addition, retention in storage ponds will stabilize putrescible wastes to varying degrees depending on the length of the retention period. Temporary storage and programmed release of wastes has been used in this country by the pulp and paper industry and in Europe by the potash industry.[20]

Industrial Process and Product
Adjustments and Reclamation of Wastes

Industrial wastes play such a large role in water pollution that procedures to reduce the amount of wastes produced per unit of product can have a highly significant effect. Many procedures of process and product adjustment and waste reclamation are technically possible. The possible scope of such measures is illustrated by a recent study of differences in the BOD of wastes *per unit of product* in Germany. Investigation of 14 paper mills indicated a population equivalent BOD ranging from 51 to 1,254 per ton of paper produced, a multiple of almost 25. Multiples computed from the ranges reported in other industries were also large—2.5 in malt factories, 6 in starch factories, 4 and 50 respectively for beef and pork slaughter houses, about 10

[20] See Friedrich Sierp, *Gewerbliche und Industrielle Abwaesser* (Berlin: Springer-Verlag, 1959); and Daniel A. Okun and James C. Lamb III. "A Waste Control Program for a River with a Highly Variable Flow," a paper presented at the 17th Purdue Industrial Waste Conference, May 1–3, 1962.

in tanneries, and about 20 in textile factories.[21] Major examples of waste load adjustment through process changes can be found in a variety of industries here and abroad.[22]

A product change to reduce residual material is called for by the detergents legislation recently passed in Germany. The new law prohibits the marketing of so-called "hard" detergents in Germany after October 1, 1964. "Hard" detergents are those like the commonly used alkyl benzene sulfonate (ABS), which are not readily degraded by the biota in treatment plants and streams. This legislation will undoubtedly lead to the production and marketing of degradable varieties of detergents. American industry has done a great deal of research on the detergents problem, and it appears that soft detergents will soon be marketed.

There have been a number of examples where waste recovery has proved profitable in the United States, even without considering the downstream damage costs avoided. In the manufacture of synthetic phenol by the sulfonation process, liquid wastes have been essentially eliminated by process engineering, and the value of recovered materials is reported to exceed recovery costs. A few sulfite pulp mills in North America have constructed full-scale ethyl alcohol plants to convert the wood sugars in their waste liquors. (The wood sugars constitute about 50 per cent of the BOD in sulfite waste liquor.) These plants have been reported to be profitable. Actual or expected competition from other alcohol processes is reported to have kept other plants from establishing similar mills. Another and perhaps more promising possibility for waste recovery from the sulfite process is the torula fodder yeast method.[23]

Another striking example in the United States of the potential of waste reclamation is the spectacular reduction in pollution loadings attributable to some sugar beet plants in the postwar period. Accord-

[21] See W. Bucksteeg, "Problematik der Bewertung giftiger Inhaltsstoffe im Abwasser und Moeglichkeiten zur Schaffung gesicherter Bewertungsgrundlagen" (Problems in the Evaluation of Toxic Materials in Effluents and Possibilities for Obtaining Secure Evaluation Standards), *Muenchner Beitraege zur Abwasser-, Fischerei-, und Flussbiologie,* Band 6 (Muenchen: Verlag R. Oldenbourg, 1959).

[22] See chapter 7 for a discussion of the use of the procedures in the area of the German *Genossenschaften.*

[23] See A. N. Helles and M. E. Wenger, "Process Engineering in Stream Pollution Abatement," *Sewage and Industrial Wastes,* Vol. 26, No. 2, February, 1954.

ing to a 1949 estimate by Rudolfs,[24] this one small part of the food industry was contributing a population equivalent BOD of 17 million, almost 13 per cent of the BOD load of all industry. At that time one medium-sized plant might contribute organic waste equal in population equivalent to the wastes of a city of 700,000 persons. A large share of this was due to the waste liquid from the Steffens process. Many plants are now recovering monosodium glutamate and potash from the Steffens waste, and thereby helping to reduce the BOD of the waste effluent to a small fraction of what it was previously.[25]

Because process changes and waste recovery can assume such an important role in reducing waste loads generated, one of the basic problems in the economics of regional waste disposal systems is how these procedures can be combined in an optimal fashion. This question is addressed in several of the following chapters.

Other Measures

Reaeration of rivers may be used as an alternative to higher levels of treatment, flow augmentation, etc. In addition to turbine aeration, several sizable mobile aerating devices are either in use or under construction. These devices can be put into use at points where critical oxygen conditions develop.[26] By raising the dissolved oxygen in such a stretch of stream, they can prevent anaerobic conditions or fish kills from developing. Reaeration differs from both orthodox treatment and increased dilution in that nothing is removed from the water, and there is no increase in flow velocity to alter the length and shape of the oxygen sag. When critical conditions are of short duration and limited in geographic scope, artificial reaeration may be as effective as other alternatives in preventing critically low levels of oxygen.

[24] William Rudolfs (ed.), *Industrial Wastes: Their Disposal and Treatment,* ACS Monograph No. 118 (Valley Stream, New York: L. E. C., Inc., 1953).
[25] Based on a conversation with Mr. Lloyd T. Jensen, Vice President of Great Western Sugar and Chairman of the Technical Task Committee on Industrial Wastes appointed by the Surgeon General.
[26] A device of this kind is currently in use or on a standby basis in the Illinois River. Also several aeration devices of various kinds are used below the Nine Springs treatment plant of the Madison Metropolitan Sewerage District. The Emschergenossenschaft in the Ruhr area of Germany has a mobile mechanical reaeration device under construction.

Wastes can, of course, be disposed of by methods which keep them from entering watercourses. Irrigation with sewage effluents is a long-established measure of this character, as are various means of disposing of domestic wastes in a more or less dry state. Among the many cities in the western United States that use all or part of their sewage effluents for irrigation are: Tucson in Arizona, Bakersfield, Fresno, San Bernardino, and San Francisco in California, and over 200 towns in Texas including Abilene, Kingsville, Lubbock, Midland, San Angelo, and San Antonio. There seems to be much further scope for this practice in our arid areas. Considerable research has been done on spray irrigation as a means of disposal of wastes from such industries as pulp and paper mills and dairies and canneries. Some facilities of this kind are in operation.

Where the quality of public water supplies is the primary consideration, alternative sources of supply can technically be substituted for sewage treatment and water supply treatment. This might involve transportation of surface supplies, tapping of groundwater supplies, and/or artificial recharge of groundwaters.

CONCLUDING COMMENTS

This discussion has greatly simplified many aspects of water quality control and completely neglected others. One point, however, is clear. Technically, there are a great variety of alternative measures available for quality control. These substitute for one another economically at various rates depending upon circumstances and upon the particular pollutants under consideration. Furthermore, it is clear that on technical grounds alone decisions concerning the proper extent of application and proper balance among control measures cannot be made rationally. Accordingly, values must be introduced into the decision-making process.

In most instances, the determination of values and the subsequent decisions concerning resource allocation and use are left to market processes in the U.S. economy. Waste disposal, however, has certain characteristics which make it undesirable for society to rely solely upon the market for decisions on quality control. One of these is the lack of independence of costs and production opportunities between economic units. Such independence is an essential element for the normative results often attributed to free markets. Since the damages of waste disposal into water courses are imposed not on the discharging unit but on another economic unit downstream, waste disposal establishes a direct, or technological, link between economic units (industrial, commercial, and household). Largely for this reason, intervention can be justified by the desirability of moving actual market results more closely into line with ideal market results. Further, however, under some circumstances there may be grounds for considering values not arising from market-type valuation at all. The next chapter elaborates on these matters.

One additional point must first be made, however. Many of the relationships and processes sketched in this chapter appear simple when presented in basic outline. Actually, most of them are extremely complex, and many of them are only poorly understood. The economic and other social results of using most of the devices and procedures described are still much less well understood. Many problems remain in forecasting the technical, physical, and economic results of waste disposal and of procedures for its control. Some of these will be identified in the subsequent discussion.[27]

[27] A more systematic survey of research needs will be found in Kneese, *op. cit.*

Part II

Economic Efficiency, Social Costs, and Equity

~~~~~~

The limit on water quality in our regions is essentially an economic one. Although further technological advance may permit us to obtain a better quality of water with a smaller expenditure of resources, the controlling question will continue to be, "How much of society's resources shall we devote to maintaining and improving water quality?"

This section is primarily aimed at developing certain basic ideas of economic theory in specific application to problems of water quality management. For the sake of simplicity it is assumed that no economies can be achieved by collective water supply and waste disposal facilities serving separate economic units such as industrial plants and municipalities. In later chapters, however, it is pointed out that certain abatement measures can often be used efficiently only on a large scale and not by individual water users and waste dischargers. Examples of such measures are low-flow augmentation, mechanical aeration of streams, treatment of entire streams, and treatment in collective plants of wastes gathered from diverse sources.

The situation presented in this section is one in which there are several water users along a stream. These water users are close enough together and the amount of dilution water is small enough for the costs of downstream users or the range of opportunities available to them to be significantly affected by upstream waste disposal. However, the water users are not close enough together to make treating their wastes in common treatment plants a feasible procedure. Also, technical or economic factors make it impractical to augment flow during low streamflow periods. The alternative ways of adjusting water quality which *are* available in the region include all forms of treatment of water or waste water at the individual water supply intake and waste water outfall, temporary lagooning of wastes, adjustments of manufacturing output, adjustment of industrial processes, temporary shutdown of industrial plants, and longer-run measures such as adjustments of industrial locations and changes in the location of industrial or municipal outfalls.

Another simplification that pervades not only this section but most of the whole study is the assumption that water is not scarce. In the arid West, of course, water itself, and not just water with certain quality characteristics, *is* subject to shortage. The analysis, as the next chapter points out, can readily be adapted to such a situation. But in this part of the book the analysis applies to humid regions (or at least to the major streams in them) and not, without the necessary adaption, to arid ones. In other words, the focus is upon situations where external diseconomies are due to degradation associated with waste discharge and not to depletion.

In general, this study is not concerned with the costs incurred in moving water to a final user or in draining a metropolis or industrial premises. While important problems of efficiency are presented by the planning and operation of delivery and drainage systems, consideration of them is limited here to the possibility that the relocation of points of intake and discharge may sometimes be an efficient alternative to other quality control measures. The focus of this study is upon water quality in the streams of a region and the optimum measures for its management.

Chapter 3 briefly explains why reliance on *private* incentives and competitive markets to allocate productive resources generally produce results that have *social* merit; it then points out why and how this allocative process may be distorted when watercourses are used for waste disposal. This form of market failure occurs because water quality deterioration produces "technological external diseconomies." These terms, traditionally used in economic theory, are explained in some detail in order to set the stage for their use later in the book. The definition of property rights in water and legal adversary proceedings are briefly evaluated as ways of handling external diseconomies. The possibility of enlarging firms so as to "internalize" the undesirable external effects and thus have them directly weighed in private decisions is also assessed.

The apparent deficiencies of these procedures lead to an examination in chapter 4 of what might be called public administrative procedures. These include effluent charges based on imposed damages and the more traditional procedure of effluent standards. Following an outline of the underlying analysis and knowledge of costs that are needed if effluent charges or standards are to achieve optimal control at individual points of waste discharge, attention is given to some of the more difficult problems encountered in making the requisite cost measurements.

Chapter 5 is a study of comparative programs of quality management in a situation where the primary problem is seeing to it that offsite costs are considered in the decisions of private firms and municipalities.

The even more complex problem of taking account of opportunities to reduce costs of regional water quality management programs by the use of collective facilities that provide services for more than one firm or local unit of government is addressed in Part III.

3

Water Pollution and Resources Allocation by Private Markets

~~~~~~

THE "WELFARE MAXIMIZING" RESULTS OF MARKET PROCESSES

Most economists view a well-functioning market system as an efficient device for allocating resources in correspondence with consumer wants.[1] If markets are highly competitive and consumers and producers are rationally attempting to achieve the greatest possible benefit for themselves, the available resources will be allocated in a way that maximizes welfare given the distribution of income.

In such an economy each productive resource will be used up to the point where the cost of an additional unit is just equal to its contribution to the value of production. For example, in the case of labor a firm will hire additional workers until the wage paid to the last worker employed just equals the dollar value of the extra product he produces. Up to that point each worker will have added more to the firm's revenues than to its costs. Now if this condition prevails in each firm and if the price of labor is uniform as between any two firms (which it would tend to be if resources are mobile), the last unit of labor used

[1] No attempt is made here to set out the theory underlying this judgment in any extensive detail. Some excellent discussions are available. See, for example, John V. Krutilla, *Multiple Purpose River Development* (Baltimore: The Johns Hopkins Press, for Resources for the Future, Inc., 1958), chapter 2; Richard H. Leftwich, *The Price System and Resource Allocation* (New York: Rinehart & Co., Inc., 1960), chapter XV; and William Baumol, *Economic Theory and Operations Research* (New York: John Wiley & Sons, 1958).

in each firm will contribute an identical value of product. Thus, if the wage for a given quality of labor is uniform in the market, the value of the product of the last unit of that type of labor hired in any one activity will be equal to that of the last unit hired in any other activity. This is important because it means that the market price paid for a resource represents the product which that resource could have generated in another line of activity. For example, if a firm hires an additional unit of labor for one dollar, production elsewhere is reduced by one dollar owing to the withdrawal of that unit of labor. As the "welfare economist" puts it, the market price of the resource is equal to its opportunity cost.

Consumers attempting to achieve maximum satisfaction from a given amount of income tend to allocate their expenditures so that the last dollar spent for any particular item will yield an amount of satisfaction equal to the last dollar spent on any other item. When this condition exists, it follows that the market price of a particular commodity reflects its worth, or goodness, or power to satisfy wants. If the unit price of one commodity is twice as high as that of another commodity, the last unit of the higher priced commodity which an individual buys must yield twice as much satisfaction as the last unit of the lower priced one. Consequently, the relative market prices of goods reflect the valuation that consumers place upon the purchase of marginal units.

If, in addition, the distribution of purchasing power conforms to the ethical standards of the community and if consumer sovereignty over resource allocation is accepted as ethically correct, the prices of goods and factors of production accurately represent their contributions to social welfare. Thus prices provide automatic, socially valid guidelines for investment and production. For example, assume that a dollar's worth of labor can be moved from an activity where it yields a dollar's worth of product to another activity where it yields more than a dollar's worth of product because the cost of the last unit of labor in that activity is not yet equal to the value of product it yields. Not only does private benefit maximization indicate and induce a shift of labor under these circumstances, but when the shift is made both the total value of production and the total satisfaction derived by society from its use of resources are increased.

In highly idealized form these notions provide a social justification for market processes and a possible justification for public intervention in instances where some obstruction prevents private market processes from equating marginal social costs and benefits.

For ideal market results, technical conditions of production and consumption must be such that the costs and benefits of performing a given act fall upon the unit performing it. If some costs can be shifted to other units, the private costs incurred do not correspond to the social cost of production as expressed by the value of production foregone, and resource allocation is distorted even though markets function in an otherwise ideal fashion. Should, for example, the employment of a mother result in the delinquency of her children, private costs of the employer (i.e., the wage) would equal only part of the social costs, which in this case might include property damages, extra police, etc. Indirect effects of this character are variously called "spillover effects," "third-party effects," or more traditionally, "external diseconomies."

Spillover effects are generally felt to be insufficient to negate the tendency toward optimal resource allocation resulting from free markets. In specific areas, however, these effects are significant and may require correction via public policy. Waste disposal into watercourses is one of these areas.

In most instances, the physical character of waste disposal is such that virtually the entire resulting damages and attendant costs are external to the unit actually discharging the wastes. Consequently, important divergences between private and social costs can arise, full social marginal costs may not be considered in making private decisions, and various significant departures from ideal resource allocation can occur.

TECHNOLOGICAL EXTERNAL DISECONOMIES

Water pollution, and smoke nuisance are economists' classic examples of "technological external diseconomies." This rather formidable phraseology can perhaps be best explained by considering each term independently, starting with the last. "Diseconomy" clearly means the result is uneconomical, i.e., that it involves higher costs or less valuable production than some other alternative. "External" refers to the incidence of the diseconomy. It means that the costs of a particular course of action, which may be in the form of an actual outlay, a reduction in income or satisfaction, or even completely foregone opportunities, are borne by an economic decision unit (say, a firm) which is managerially independent from the one pursuing the course of action. "Technological" means that this cost is transferred from one unit to another managerially independent unit by a technical or physical linkage between production processes.[2]

When such technological links are "internal" to a decision unit, the result may be considerably different than if they are external. To take a simple example, a farmer may find that a small stream on his property will irrigate either an upstream plot A or a downstream plot B, but not both. If plot A is irrigated, plot B cannot be watered. In deciding whether to irrigate plot A, the farmer will consider the return lost on plot B, and plot A will be irrigated only if its return is higher. Consequently, the resource will be allocated in the way that maximizes the value of production. If, however, plot B is on another farmer's land and the owner of plot A cannot sell his right to the water, the owner of plot A will not consider the return lost on plot B in determining whether to irrigate plot A. If plot B actually presents the superior productive opportunity, failure to irrigate it because the water is preempted upstream is a technological external diseconomy.

Now suppose that the owner of plot A *can* sell his right to the water and that the farmer owning plot B can afford to, and has an incentive to, pay more for the water than it is worth if applied on plot A. In this case, the efficient result would once again be produced.

But suppose that a third farmer appears who has an even more productive piece of land and can bid the water away from the owner of plot B. This means that the value of output (the social product according to the economic value theory explained above) is increased if the water is applied to the new land. In the process, however, farmer

---

[2] Many of the points discussed in the remainder of this chapter are treated in greater detail in Allen V. Kneese, "Rationalizing Water Supply Quality Decisions in Urban Industrial Areas," a paper presented at Second Conference on Urban Public Expenditures, Feb. 21-22, 1964, sponsored by the Committee on Urban Economics of Resources for the Future, Inc. For an extended discussion of external economies and diseconomies, see Roland N. McKean, *Efficiency in Government Through Systems Analysis* (New York: John Wiley & Sons, 1958), chapter 8.

B suffers a loss because he is "priced out of the market." Such a cost or loss is frequently referred to as a "pecuniary" diseconomy, which has a considerably different significance from that of "technological" ones. In the former case the supply price of a factor of production (in our example, water) rises because of competition for its services. The level of factor compensation reflects productivity in alternative employments. Accordingly, no distortion of resources allocation results from the purchase of factors up to the point which produces maximum profits in each independent decision unit individually.

This example also illustrates the close relationship between technological diseconomies and property rights. By altering the character of the right to the water—making it salable—the external diseconomy was eliminated. This emphasizes the fact that in dealing with the reduction in output caused by technological spillovers the possibility of adjusting property rights to permit the external opportunity costs to be internalized is among the alternatives to be considered. This method, however, appears to be of limited use in dealing with pollution-caused inefficiencies.

Where technological spillovers are significant, the type of resource misallocations that will occur can be foreseen in a general way. For example, when disposal of wastes into watercourses neglects downstream costs, the costs of some economic units are understated (apparently costless waste disposal into watercourses) and some are overstated ("excessive" imposed damages and treatment costs) relative to social (opportunity) costs. This tends to induce overproduction and overconsumption of some items and underproduction and underconsumption of others. To illustrate, when an upstream paper mill dumps its wastes into a watercourse without consideration of the downstream costs imposed, it produces paper which is artificially "cheap." In effect, nothing is paid for the use of a valuable resource, i.e., for the waste dilution, degradation, and carriage capacity of the watercourse. From a social point of view, the value of this resource is measured by the alternative uses which can be made of the water. *Failure of municipal and industrial waste dischargers to consider that subsequent water uses may be made more expensive or foreclosed entirely by the discharge is perhaps the basic element of the pollution problem.*

When the offsite costs are not considered, an excessive amount of waste tends to be deposited in receiving waters, little effort is made to treat waste water, to recover materials from waste water, or to design and operate industrial processes so as to conserve materials. That process engineering and materials recovery processes can effectively reduce waste loads has been richly demonstrated in this country and in West Germany (see chapter 7). Moreover, studies of waste loads generated per unit of physical output by plants producing identical goods by different processes suggest the degree to which wastes can be engineered away. This emphasizes the importance of providing the appropriate incentives for such procedures. *A society that allows waste dischargers to neglect the offsite costs of waste disposal will not only devote too few resources to the treatment of waste but will also produce too much waste in view of the damage it causes.* In a general way this may be considered the rationale for some form of social or political intervention in waste disposal decisions.

Free markets, however, do not inevitably result in neglect of downstream costs by waste disposers. Assume, for example, that a firm which produces a waste material toxic to fish is considering location on the banks of a stream where a downstream firm is engaged in commercial fishing. The stream has no other users. Assume further that the fishing firm realizes an annual return of 10, and that it uses transferable resources with a value of 100 and no fixed capital. Assume for simplicity also that the resources it uses can be transferred at no cost to other productive uses. "Transferable resources" means those not specialized to the production of a particular product. In the present example, no specialized resources are used. "Transfer" may or may not involve physical relocation of resources.

The fishing firm will be willing to pay up to 10 annually to prevent the other firm from putting its waste materials into the stream to an extent which would kill the fish. It is, of course, assumed that the toxic waste is strictly a by-product of some productive process. The possibility of some enterprising individual threatening to put toxic material in the stream merely to collect the 10 is thus excluded.

In the simplest case where the fish are simply killed or not killed, the firm with the potentially lethal wastes will either accept 10 and not kill the fish (by treating its wastes or not locating on the stream) or else simply kill the fish. If it is calculating rationally and kills the fish, this must mean that it would cost more than 10 not to do so. Consequently, the polluting firm's cost saving plus the value of production from the transferred resources is greater than the value of continuing to fish in the stream. The result will be precisely the same as though a public agency had imposed the offsite social cost (10) of killing the fish upon the polluting firm. The firm would still kill them if it costs more than 10 not to kill them, and it would not kill them if it does not.[3] In either case, the net value of fishing becomes an "opportunity cost" to the firm. The two results are the same *only* from the point of view of allocating resources to their best use. Income distribution would, of course, be different under the two situations. Moreover, on equity grounds it might be considered justifiable to compensate the fisherman for his loss of the opportunity to fish. This point is considered later.

An additional point to be made here is that the social cost of killing the fish is 10, not 110 (market value of the fish), as is often implied in exhortations to assess polluters with the cost of damages they cause. If a charge of 110 were levied on the firm discharging wastes into the stream, the allocation of resources would be distorted because the polluting firm would be induced to spend up to 110 in treatment, net cost of waste recovery or locational disadvantage in order to avoid killing fish with a net social value of 10. The waste discharge might indeed kill $110 worth of fish, but, by our assumption, it would release $100 worth of resources for alternative uses. Thus while the waste discharge would result in a drop of $110 in the output of fish, it would result in an increase of $100 in the output of some other things. As a result, there would be a net loss of $10 of total output.

A more realistic situation is one in which treatment (waste recovery, process changes, etc.) and fish kills can be varied continuously. In this case the fishing firm would be willing to pay an amount up to the net value of fishing in that particular location for each relevant level of fish kills avoided. Similarly the firm would be willing to pay up to the net value of damage avoided for removal of phenols or other substances that impart undesirable flavors and thereby reduce the market value of the fish.

Figure 3 illustrates a situation where the damaged party sees to it that

[3] For an elaboration of this point see R. H. Coase, "The Problem of Social Cost," *Journal of Law and Economics*, October, 1960.

the waste discharger views the net offsite cost associated with his waste disposal as an opportunity cost. The incremental cost of the optimum combination of waste reduction measures is *AE*. The damage cost per unit of waste is *Y*. Under these circumstances, if the waste discharger is either paid *Y* dollars for each unit of waste withheld or charged *Y* dollars for each unit of waste discharged, he will withhold *X* units of waste. At this point, waste reduction has resulted in a saving to the discharger of *YAB* or, if a payment for withholding wastes is made, a net revenue of *YAB*. Beyond this point it is less costly for him to discharge the waste and either pay the charge or forego the payment.

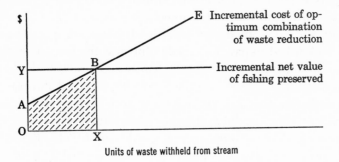

Figure 3.

It is also at point *X* that total costs associated with waste disposal (abatement costs plus damage costs) are at a minimum. If abatement were carried an increment further the resource cost of the additional abatement would exceed the resource cost saved (i.e. total costs would rise). If abatement were reduced incrementally the cost of additional damages would exceed the cost of the additional abatement (i.e. total costs associated with waste disposal would rise). One may alternatively refer to the damages (costs) avoided as benefits and the costs incurred for abatement as costs and say that waste reduction up to but not beyond point *X* will maximize benefits minus costs. Cost minimization (including damages as a cost) and net benefit maximization are in this case completely synonymous.

Thus it is possible for market transactions to avoid the resources misallocations that could result from externalities, but such transactions are not always easy (inexpensive) to organize. The damaging effects of water pollution are so widespread and diffuse, especially in highly developed areas, that establishing a market which would permit the minimization of production costs at optimum output would be very complex (expensive).[4] As a rule, such markets do not become established.

PROPERTY RIGHTS, LEGAL PROCESSES, AND POLLUTION

The point was made earlier that there is a close relation between the nature of property rights and the occurrence of external diseconomies. Is it possible to structure property rights in water in such a way that upstream waste dischargers will take appropriate account of downstream costs? In the example used above, the party benefiting from the fish had to pay. Presumably this was the case either because the law specified that the waste discharger had a right to discharge his wastes into the stream regardless of damages caused downstream or because the law specified nothing about such rights and the upstream discharger simply exploited his physically superior position. An alternative possibility and one more generally consistent with the principles of riparian water law is that the upstream user is liable for damage downstream.[5]

To reiterate an earlier point, the definition of damages is highly important if efficient behavior is to result from actual or potential damage claims. To repeat part of the earlier example, if an award of 110 were made to the downstream fisherman for fish killed by the up-

---

[4] Difficulties for the "market solution" also arise from interaction between damage and cost functions due to "non-separability" in externalities and when damage functions are non-linear and multiple waste dischargers affect the same water users. Some discussion of these difficulties which also afflict "administrative" solutions is presented in the Appendix to chapter 4.

[5] "Reasonable use" interpretations of riparian doctrine have considerably altered earlier interpretations which viewed the downstream user as privileged to receive the flow of the stream "undiminished in quantity and quality." The court's definition of reasonable use has often involved a balancing of upstream and downstream use. The court's efforts to "balance equities" in cases of this kind have often involved considerations of upstream and downstream costs. In a general way the "reasonable use" interpretation of riparian right is consistent with the conceptual structure described in this chapter. Significant elements of "prior appropriations doctrine" have also crept into the water law of the riparian states (generally those of the humid East and Midwest). See Jacob H. Beuscher, "Appropriation Water Law Elements in Riparian Doctrine States," *Buffalo Law Review*, No. 10, 1961.

stream waste discharge, costs (resource use) would be increased by more than the net value of the fish. The upstream firm would be induced to spend up to 110 in treatment, net cost of waste recovery, or in locational disadvantage in order to avoid killing fish with a net value of 10.

Presuming, however, that the law of property were to be framed so that damages avoided were always "net," [6] could optimal water quality management programs be expected to occur? [7]

Three major deficiencies of legal remedies are listed below. Some of their implications will be clarified by subsequent discussion.

1. Adversary proceedings involving private parties are at best a cumbersome procedure, and, if the law is enforced with any degree of precision, delays in deciding cases might themselves cause substantial inefficiencies.

2. The diffuse effects of damages associated with waste disposal would make it hard to bring suit for the full damages. Many hundreds of recreationists may be damaged. Costs may be imposed on numerous water diverters as well. Many of them may have their costs increased only slightly, but the aggregate costs may still be large. This is analogous to the difficulties mentioned earlier of dealing with the problem via private payment mechanisms.

3. Water pollution imposes costs in a highly variable fashion over time. This means that the most efficient result can often be achieved by measures which are put to use, or high levels of use, only periodically. It would appear to be difficult to frame laws with sufficient flexibility to permit realization of such efficiencies.

---

[6] If resources, especially labor, are highly immobile the "net" loss (gross loss minus value of resources in alternative uses) may approach gross loss. However, one may well echo Eckstein's statement in this connection ". . . in a capitalist system, in which the movement of resources into their proper places is accomplished through the existence of differentials in reward, policies cannot be predicated on a general denial of mobility. Policies which reduce mobility, such as removal of the differentials which are to induce movement, destroy the foundations on which the viability of the system rests." Otto Eckstein, *Water-Resource Development: The Economics of Project Evaluation* (Cambridge: Harvard University Press, 1961), p. 209.

[7] The present discussion continues to be only about situations where no significant economies can be realized through provision of collective facilities for different economic and/or local political units. Where the latter situation occurs, legal remedies alone cannot lead to optimal results.

"INTERNALIZING" THE EXTERNALITIES IN A FIRM

The suggestion has sometimes been advanced that, since technological externalities permit higher aggregate profits when production processes are jointly planned and operated, mergers will take place until a "natural" decision unit is established.[8] However, with respect to water pollution in a highly developed basin, the technical ties between, say, any given pair of production processes located at different points will probably be comparatively weak despite the fact that in total the external diseconomies are large. The planning and operation of spatially separate and technologically diverse production processes poses complexities for management and therefore is not costless. Consequently, externalities would tend not to be fully internalized even though aggregate profit could be increased in this way if integration were costless.

The term "natural decision unit" is deceptively simple, since different decision units are "natural" for different functions. Thus the term "optimum" decision unit would seem to be preferable to "natural" decision unit. The natural decision unit idea has probably gained impetus from the fact that discussion has frequently been in terms of two decision units strongly connected by technological ties but otherwise operating in an environment free of externalities. Moreover, the internalization of externalities into a private decision-making unit over an entire basin would most probably result in changes in market structure (monopolization) contrary to social policy and inconsistent with efficient production because of its market power.

[8] The problem of how the size of the firm (the basic production decision unit in a market economy) is determined has been frequently discussed in the economic literature. One line of discussion has concerned itself with diseconomies of scale for the production of a single product. Another has addressed the question of how the number of products entering into the output of a firm is established. See R. H. Coase, "The Nature of the Firm," *Economica*, Vol. IV, 1937. This article was reprinted in American Economic Association, *Readings in Price Theory* (Homewood, Illinois: Richard Irvin, Inc., 1952). George Stigler has observed that when production functions are technically related there may exist motivation for merger. See *Production and Distribution Theories* (New York: Macmillan Company, 1946). The most recent suggestion that externalities give rise to "natural" decision units which "internalize" them is found in Otto A. Davis and Andrew Whinston, "Externalities, Welfare, and the Theory of Games," *Journal of Political Economy*, June, 1962, pp. 241ff.

Nevertheless some clarification of concepts may be gained by considering a simple, hypothetical case in which the externalities are internalized even though in actuality this cannot be considered either a feasible or a desirable solution. Assume that a single firm with two plants is the sole commercial user of a stream which is also valuable for sport fishing. Assume that the firm controls access to the stream and can levy charges for recreation use, that it is able to charge each fisherman the amount he is willing to pay rather than go without the opportunity to fish, and that it buys all its inputs and sells all its other outputs in competitive markets.[9]

Waste Disposal

If this firm attempts to maximize its profits, which under our assumption is the same as maximizing net social return, how will it manage its water utilization? Since it operates two plants on the same stream, the firm will have an incentive to take into account the effects of upstream activities on the downstream plant. (The negative downstream effects are termed damage costs.) While damage costs are focused upon in this volume, the possibility of favorable effects from effluent discharges is not excluded. If, for example, the upstream plant A uses large quantities of water for cooling and its effluent consequently warms the stream, the downstream plant may benefit if its processes require warm water.

Presume, however, that plant A produces a waste material which is toxic to fish and damaging to plant B in proportion to its concentration.[10] For simplicity, assume initially that the only quality control procedure available at plant A is effluent treatment and that the pollutant is non-degradable. The considerations entering into the profit-maximizing behavior of the firm are portrayed by the curves in Figure 4. At point X the firm will be discharging the amount of waste which under the stated conditions is optimum.

[9] These restrictions will be meaningful to economists but need not detain other readers. Briefly the reason for them is to assure that marginal revenue equals price for all outputs and that the marginal cost of acquiring factors equals their price or wage.

[10] For purposes of the present example it is assumed that plant B does not produce a waste discharge. Some of the complexities that might result if it did are discussed in Appendix I to chapter 4.

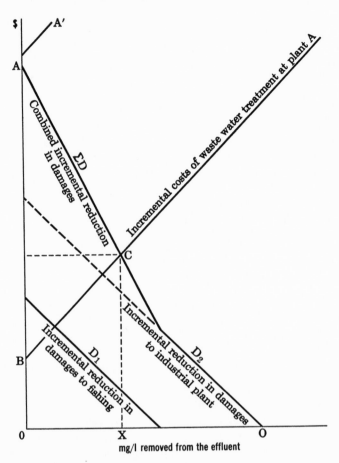

Figure 4.

A word of explanation is in order about the pictured functions. First of all, the abscissa indicates the number of mg/1 of the pollutant removed in treatment. The incremental cost of treatment simply shows how much total treatment costs rise with the removal of additional units of waste. The damage functions indicate how much damages are reduced at the margin when treatment is increased by an increment. The damages are added vertically (i.e. for a given concentration, the dollar value of D_1 and D_2 are summed) because, in considering how much to treat, damages to both uses which are affected in a complementary way by treatment must be taken into account. ΣD represents the increment in damages avoided when treatment is increased by an increment.[11] For simplicity the functions are shown as linear—no change in principles occurs if they are curved.

Under the circumstances pictured, the firm would find it profitable to continue treating the wastes at the upstream outfall until X mg/1 are removed. If the firm did slightly less than this, marginal damage costs would exceed incremental treatment costs and it would pay to advance treatment. If the firm treated beyond X, incremental treatment costs would exceed incremental damage costs avoided, and it would pay to reduce treatment and permit higher damages. X is thus the optimum level of water quality in the sense that the costs associated with waste disposal are at a minimum there. These costs include both *damage costs* and *abatement costs*.[12]

Alternatively, one can say that the net benefits to the firm of abating its upstream pollution are at a maximum at this concentration. As previously indicated this is a fully equivalent statement if we term the damages avoided by waste treatment "benefits" and the costs of treatment "costs." These terminological matters will take on more importance when public policy comes under discussion. At this point it may

---

[11] A discussion of principles involved in this adding together approach may be found in George S. Tolley and V. S. Hastings, "Optimal Water Allocations, The North Platte River," *Quarterly Journal of Economics*, May, 1960. A much earlier discussion is found in Howard R. Bowen, *Toward Social Economy* (New York: Rinehart & Co., 1948), pp. 176–79.

[12] The results indicated above can also be stated in terms of the differential calculus. The firm confronts two damage functions D_1 and D_2 and a treatment cost function TC. The following conditions hold:

$$D_1 = f_1(R) \qquad f_1^1 < 0$$
$$D_2 = f_2(R) \qquad f_2^1 < 0$$
$$TC = f_3(R) \qquad f_3^1 > 0.$$

The objective (objective function) is to minimize

$$Z = D_1 + D_2 + TC = f_1(R) + f_2(R) + f_3(R),$$

which will be the case when

$$\frac{dZ}{dR} = f_1^1(R) + f_2^1(R) + f_3^1(R) = 0,$$

if

$$\frac{d^2Z}{dR^2} > 0.$$

be noted that the author prefers the cost minimization terminology (remembering that costs include all damage costs) because it calls attention to the fact that pollution abatement is primarily a matter of avoiding costs. More importantly, the terminology is very convenient at later points when water quality "standards" are discussed.

One other possibility should be mentioned here. If incremental costs of abatement were at the level of A' the firm would not undertake any waste reduction effort because incremental costs would exceed incremental benefits. This is a case where it is simply less costly to endure water quality deterioration than to do anything about it.

If we permit the firm more alternative ways of reducing its waste load, the principles do not change. Say, for example, that plant A could, in addition to treating wastes, cut back on its output, introduce process adjustments, change the location of its plant, etc. In order to minimize costs associated with waste disposal, the firm would still have to "trade off" between alternatives until their incremental or marginal costs are equated (i.e., $MC_A = MC_B = \ldots = MC_N = MC$ of pollution damages).

Water "Shortage" [13]

Water itself may have a scarcity value, as was implied in the irrigation example used earlier in this chapter to illustrate the character of technological and pecuniary external diseconomies. Should our hypothetical firm be located on a stream where flows fall low enough to deprive downstream users of water supplies or if the quality of water is significantly impaired by depleting activities that reduce the dilution water, then the firm must consider not only the increased costs and decreased opportunities to earn money occasioned by its waste disposal, but also the effect of its upstream depletion through evaporation. The principles are precisely the same as those for waste disposal: the costs incurred downstream as a result of upstream depletion must be weighed against the cost of measures to reduce depletion upstream (cutback or shutdown of production, dry processes, alternative means of cooling, etc.). Many of these water-saving measures may also reduce

[13] See also M. Mason Gaffney, "Comparison of Pricing and other Means of Allocating Water Resources," *Water Law and Policy in the Southeast,* Institute of Law and Governments, University of Georgia, Athens, 1962.

waste loads (for example, cutting back on production). When this is the case, the joint marginal value of higher flow and fewer residual waste products must be determined and weighed against the cost of the upstream measure. When costs are truly joint it is not helpful to rational decision making to try to allocate them; the joint results of an action must be jointly evaluated and weighed against the costs of the action.

SOME GENERAL POINTS

Water uses that do not cause any productive opportunities to be foregone are socially costless. For example, uses that do not change quantity, quality, or flow pattern do not impose offsite costs. Imposition of any charge or other restriction on this sort of use would lead to a misallocation of resources since other opportunities are neither foregone nor made more expensive by it. It is difficult to think of any use which has *precisely* this characteristic. However, in many instances, the opportunities foregone or costs imposed because of a water use may be insignificant.

In humid areas, water uses impose downstream opportunity costs primarily through their impact on water quality. This is true of uses that deplete the water flow and those that alter flow patterns. In all cases where streams contain natural impurities, these uses alter the quality of water downstream whether there is municipal and industrial waste disposal into the stream or not.

Waste disposal is a productive use of water resources. To the degree that it is less costly than alternative courses of action when all offsite costs are considered, *it saves* resources and permits higher levels of production and consumption than would be possible if this resource use were prohibited or highly restricted. The problem is that private markets do not automatically measure and bring to bear at relevant points of decision the full costs of this resource use and that adjudicating property rights to accomplish this end is likely to be cumbersome and inefficient. Also adversary proceedings will fail to represent the value of certain water uses. Consequently, in the following chapter some possible modes of public intervention are explored in light of the concept of economic efficiency as it has been developed up to this point.

4

Causing Offsite Costs to be Reflected in Waste Disposal Decisions

~~~~~~

Under a free market economy municipalities and private firms not only can escape certain costs associated with waste disposal by passing the problem further downstream, but find it to their economic advantage to do so. The ultimate costs throughout a whole watershed are not reduced—in fact, they are increased if offsite costs exceed the costs of reducing waste discharge—but they are borne by someone other than the discharger. As we have already seen, this neglect of offsite costs would be removed if a single firm managed all phases of water supply and use throughout an entire basin and if there were no public goods involved; then the external diseconomies would become internal. While the basin-wide firm idea is very useful to illuminate the character and role of external diseconomies, it has already been explained that in actuality such a solution would be deficient and undesirable. However, several forms of public intervention can, at least to a considerable degree, cause offsite costs to be reflected in the waste disposal decisions of individual firms and of local government units.

Possible measures of this kind—effluent charges, incentive payments, and enforcement of quality standards—are considered in this chapter from the economic viewpoint. Discussion of political and administrative details of just what kind of organization might do the intervening, and by what means, is reserved for chapter 8.

In highly developed areas the offsite costs associated with unregulated waste discharge are likely to be great enough to justify public regulation, despite the costs and distortions which may be entailed in the regulation itself.[1] Here the focus is on the economic aspects of dealing with the external costs of waste discharge, and the assumption is made that regulatory public authorities exist and that they have sufficient geographical scope to internalize the major external costs associated with waste discharge in their areas. It is also assumed that these agencies, which are generally referred to as "river basin authorities," have as their objective obtaining the maximum net benefit from the water resources.

In general, benefits are taken to be determined by willingness to pay for goods and services, and costs by the value of foregone production opportunities.[2]

How can the individual municipality or industry be induced to consider offsite costs in its decisions involving waste generation, treatment, and discharge? This question is discussed, first, in terms of the method to be used. Emphasis is placed on a device whereby the basin authority would levy charges on effluent discharge. The alternative possibility of framing a system of payments for waste discharge reduction to achieve optimum water quality is also discussed.

Attention is then directed to the variety of considerations involved in actually determining the costs associated with a given waste discharge. How can the effects of hydrologic variability be reflected in a system of effluent charges? Can the value of recreational, aesthetic, and public health uses be measured? How can the effluent charges system be applied when a receiving water quality standard is imposed to reflect a value which cannot be measured explicitly? What arrangements can be made to deal with situations where an abatement measure has a joint effect on two or more polluting substances? Finally, the systems of effluent charges or payments are compared with the traditional regulation device—effluent standards.

---

[1] As judged in terms of the criteria of economic welfare theory. See James M. Buchanan, "Politics, Policy and the Pigovian Margins," *Economica*, February, 1962.

[2] Additional assumptions are that actions by the authority do not alter the relative distribution of income, and that markets generally are sufficiently competitive to produce prices close to marginal costs. Under these circumstances prices generally provide measures of social value (exceptions are noted later).

ECONOMIC INCENTIVES FOR REDUCING
WASTE DISCHARGE [3]

Economists have long held that technological spillovers can be counteracted by levying taxes on the unit "responsible" for the diseconomy and by paying a subsidy to the "damaged" party. Some have even demonstrated that under certain conditions the appropriate tax is just large enough to pay the appropriate subsidy.[4] This idea makes a good bit of sense when one views the uneconomic effects of spillovers as resulting basically from a maldistribution of costs. However, in the case of water pollution, and from the point of view of resources allocation, it is not necessary to both levy a tax and pay a subsidy. This *can* be done, but either a charge on effluents or a payment to reduce discharge will serve to achieve the combination of measures that will minimize the costs associated with waste disposal in a region. Interestingly enough, if a payment is made it must be paid to the waste discharger for reducing his discharge. The decision to use a payment or a charge depends, therefore, not on the ability or inability of either to achieve the efficiency objective, but on notions of equity, acceptability, and cost of administration. From the efficiency point of view, it is essential that the waste disposer consider downstream costs as opportunity costs in making his production and waste disposal decisions. Furthermore, the downstream water user must recognize the value of the stream to upstream users for waste disposal purposes. Since the downstream user must adjust to the level of water quality in the stream, the latter results automatically if the upstream users are given the appropriate incentive to control their waste discharge to an optimum extent. For example, assume it costs only $1.00 to treat a given increment of polluting substance at the water supply intake downstream (due to some "self-purification" in the water course), but $2.00 to treat

---

[3] The matters discussed in this section are addressed in a more extensive and more formal manner in Appendix II to this chapter.

[4] James E. Meade, "External Economies and Diseconomies in a Competitive Situation," *Economic Journal*, March, 1952; and Otto A. Davis and Andrew Whinston, "Externalities, Welfare, and the Theory of Games," *Journal of Political Economy*, June, 1962. The latter article makes some important theoretical contributions which are discussed in Appendix I to this chapter.

it at a discharge point upstream, and these are the only alternatives. In this case, levying the downstream costs of $1.00 on the polluter would not cause him to treat, as he would have to use $2.00 worth of resources on treatment; the downstream user is then induced to treat, and he only uses $1.00 worth of resources.

Some of the points stated above may be clarified by referring again to the stream used only by a downstream commercial fisherman and an upstream manufacturer. If someone—say, a public agency—stood ready to discourage the discharge of waste by paying the manufacturer an amount equal to the net value of the opportunity to fish, optimum resource allocation would tend to be obtained.[5] In the example the *net* value of fishing was 10. If a payment of this amount were available to him, the profit-maximizing manufacturer would consider the 10 as an opportunity cost in making his production and waste disposal decisions. Should he find, for example, that the 10 will not cover waste treatment but that it exceeds the current return from his transferable resources, he may decide to shift his location or alter his production. Strictly from the point of view of resources allocation, it would make no difference whether an effluent charge was levied on the discharger or a payment was made to him for not discharging wastes. From the point of view of ethics or justice, it might. When references are subsequently made to payments and charges, they should be understood to mean charges levied on effluents and payments to the discharger for not discharging wastes.

While an occasional example is presented in terms of the payment technique, the presentation in most of the rest of the study is in terms of "putting the costs on the waste discharger." If costs are properly

---

[5] The result in terms of resource allocation will be the same whether a tax reflecting the marginal value to B (downstream user) is levied on the marginal activity of A (waste discharger) or whether B compensates A. However, in the absence of a payment from the affected party the solution is not "Pareto optimal," i.e., the two parties would be willing to engage in further trade if one neglects any costs associated with such trade. For a formal development of this point see James M. Buchanan and William Craig Stubblebine, "Externality," *Economica*, November, 1962, pp. 371ff. The present analysis assumes, I feel, realistically, that negotiation between individual waste dischargers and those damaged by waste discharges will be of minor importance. See also Allen V. Kneese, "Rationalizing Water Supply Quality Decisions in Urban Industrial Areas," a paper presented at Second Conference on Urban Public Expenditures, Feb. 21–22, 1964, New York, sponsored by the Committee on Urban Economics of Resources for the Future, Inc.

defined, this procedure tends to produce an optimum allocation of
resources and optimum waste loads. Moreover, charges are more likely
to agree with most people's concept of justice. Finally, and most important, the payments procedure encounters particularly difficult administrative problems. For one thing, an industrial enterprise may find
it profitable to adopt processes which generate much waste in order
to be able to accept payment for reducing discharge. Problems are
compounded when industrial location decisions or decisions to enter
or leave an industry are involved. Payments would have to be continued to a firm even if it chose going out of business as the best means
of reducing its waste discharge. Furthermore, payments would have to
be made to firms who would locate in the region if the payment were
not available. (For a further discussion of these points see Appendix II
to this chapter.)

It is worth noting again that efficient results from a system of charges
on the waste discharger do not depend upon payment of compensation
to the "damaged" party.[6] Compensation, if any, must not interfere with
efficient resource shifts by downstream parties. For example, if a given
increment in plant A's effluent discharge increases the costs to plant B,
the social cost is not necessarily the difference between what it cost
plant B to treat its water supply before and after waste discharge, but
the difference between cost without the increment of discharge and the
best alternative with it. This may mean that plant B must go to another
source, reuse its water, or possibly even shut down. Provided that plant
A is required to pay an amount equal to the social cost of each unit of
pollution it puts into the stream, the best alternative for minimizing
social costs will be chosen by plant B if it is paid no compensation.
Compensation should not be tied to a specific way of obtaining water
or to a specific use. Damages paid to the disadvantaged fisherman, for
example, should in no way be made contingent upon his continuing to
fish.

If effluent charges are levied upon the waste discharger, the question
may well arise as to what to do with the funds for which there is no
counterpart expenditure and which do not themselves present an actual
resource use. Actually, what is done with them is a matter of ethics or
equity. For example, these funds could be used to pay compensation

[6] See fn. 5.

to those "inequitably" damaged. Care must be taken, however, that the manner of disposition does not itself affect resource allocation adversely.

If it is considered desirable on equity or other grounds, a procedure could be worked out whereby the funds are paid back to the waste dischargers as a group. This might work in the following way: Each manufacturer or municipality producing a particular type of waste would be paid a lump sum per year. These payments would be calculated to exhaust the total funds paid as effluent charges by all dischargers. The individual payments might be made in proportion to assets or population, or other standard measures unrelated to waste discharge. This would leave each manufacturer with the incentive to minimize the sum of his effluent charges and cost of abatement measures (which means equating them at the margin) since this would minimize his outlays but not reduce his refund payments.[7] However, lump sum payments could result in inefficiency if the payment were contingent upon a firm continuing in business. For example, if the damage costs levied on a firm for its pollution cause the firm to operate at a loss, it should not *permanently* remain in business because the value of resources it would use is greater in other employment.[8] If the lump sum payment were made contingent upon the firm staying in business, it would have the incentive to do so, however.

The same point has already been made with respect to the use of subsidies. Going out of business would need to be considered abatement activity justifying payment. While optimum pollution control would only very infrequently involve shutdown of industrial plants, the possibility of its occurrence cannot be ignored.

Other "reasonable" procedures for achieving equity effects which are neutral in terms of efficiency can be conceived. For example, once a system is established for existing waste dischargers, the rule might be adopted that new or substantially enlarged industries or municipalities

[7] For a somewhat similar proposal with respect to the external diseconomy problem presented by pumping of a "common" ground water resource, see Edward Renshaw, "Managing Ground Water Reservoirs," *Journal of Farm Economics,* May, 1963, p. 285.

[8] It might remain until its capital equipment is depleted since only variable (operating) costs are relevant to the decision to produce or not to produce as long as capital equipment does not need replacement.

would be treated as follows: new upstream discharge which causes costs (damage costs) downstream has a charge levied upon it; any new or anticipated activity downstream which necessitates costs (abatement costs) upstream will cause a payment for waste reduction to existing upstream waste dischargers. A new activity which is located in the middle would both pay a charge and cause a payment to be made. If desired, a carefully designed charge (which did not alter resource allocation decisions) could be levied on the new downstream user to wholly or partially make the payment upstream, but, as in the case of payment of compensation to damaged users downstream, it need not be. Any deficits or surpluses resulting from procedures of this kind would have to be financed or disposed of by measures which would themselves leave resources allocation approximately undisturbed. Actually the procedure outlined would meet most of the "equity" arguments which can be readily thought of. In the first place, established waste dischargers who are not necessarily "profiting" by their waste discharge, would not have to pay a charge. Payments would, instead, be made to established companies for reducing their waste discharge.

Only new plants would have a charge levied upon them, and they presumably would take this charge into account in their initial decision to locate in the basin. Also, this plan would prevent a waste discharger's effluent charge from rising because a new plant unexpectedly locates downstream.

It must, nevertheless, be admitted that this system is more complex than a straight system of charges. It does avoid the necessity of making payments to firms which would otherwise locate in the basin but for which the comparative advantage of location there is less than the costs they would impose. However, the payment aspect of it does have the other administrative disadvantages discussed earlier, i.e., it is an invitation to extortion and requires payments to firms which have been induced to go out of business.

It is clear also that it would be very difficult to obtain universal agreement upon what constitutes "equity" in a system of charges and payments. One might argue that the owners of companies that have been discharging wastes into a stream without considering downstream costs should have foreseen the temporary character of the situation and made some provision for increased costs in their investment and location decisions. One might also argue that the possibility of having one's costs raised by a new or expanded water use downstream is a normal business risk similar to the possibility that expanded demand will raise the cost of any other scarce and therefore valuable resource.

Universal agreement is unlikely to be attained on these matters, but, as previously mentioned, it is the author's predisposition to move toward a system of charges. Payments pose more difficulties in administration, and their financing requires the levying of taxes, which, in turn, may produce distortions. Indeed, applying the payments approach in anything like an ideal manner may prove practically impossible. It must be admitted that some windfall losses will be sustained with the charges system, but this is also true of other policies aimed at improving the efficiency of the economy—anti-trust, for example. Moreover, the institution of *any* kind of regulation procedures will cause such losses to occur. When large-scale water quality management facilities can be economically applied, there is an additional, strong reason for preferring charges. This situation is the subject of Part III.

One other problem should be addressed at this point. This study generally treats the individual river basin as though *all* basins in the economy were managed with the same objectives and criteria. If this is not the case, the procedures described may give rise to non-optimum results from the viewpoint of the national economy. For example, if a particular plant is induced not to locate in basin 1 (say, by effluent charges representing downstream damages), it may locate instead in basin 2 where it is not forced to consider downstream damage costs. The damage costs in basin 2 may be even greater than in basin 1.

In principle such "out-of-the-basin" effects could be taken into account in levying charges. The difficulty is the greatly expanded information requirements of explicitly accounting for them. The cost effects of alternative feasible locations in all other basins would have to be known to assess opportunity costs correctly. It should be noted that any effort at regulation like rule-of-thumb effluent standards applied in one basin and not in others, or more stringently in some than in others, would give rise to the same type of distorting effects. Furthermore, such methods would most probably introduce additional distortions because costs in the basin are not even systematically taken into account.

In practice, taking out-of-basin effects into account would require an impossible amount of data. Since regulatory procedures of varying and difficult-to-assess stringency are in effect in other basins, the best procedure would probably be for a regional agency to operate without regard to out-of-the-basin effects.

The question remains, however, whether an over-all (national) optimum allocation would result from application of the same criteria and cost redistribution procedures *individually* in each basin. The answer appears to be that there would be a tendency toward such an optimum. All decisions with respect to the location of production and the generation and disposal of wastes would tend to reflect the opportunity cost of putting wastes into water courses, as well as such other costs as labor, materials, marketing, and transportation.

Suppose a plant can be located in either of two basins, and all its costs except waste disposal would be the same in either case. In one, the downstream costs of all possible locations are higher than in the other. If charges levied by the basin agencies accurately reflect downstream costs, the plant will locate in the basin where over-all costs are lower. Decentralized decisions based on the profit motive tend to yield minimum over-all costs of production for a given level of output.

PROBLEMS OF DETERMINING CHARGES

The Nature of Damage Functions

Basic to the effectiveness of a system of effluent charges is assessment of the "damage cost function," which is the functional relationship between an amount of a pollutant discharged and damages. The simplest situation occurs when this function is linear. In general, the present exposition will assume linear damage functions.[9] Such a situation is illustrated in Table 1, where it is assumed that five plants are arrayed along a stream, that streamflow increases along the course of the

[9] For a discussion of the problems that arise when damage functions are nonlinear, see Appendix I, p. 85.

Table 1. *Simple Illustration of Cost Distribution*

Plant no. (serially located along stream)	Chloride load discharged (lb. per day)	Chloride load at plant intake (lb. per day)	Flow Condition I				Flow Condition II			
			Streamflow (mill. gpd)	Chloride concentration (lb. per mill. gpd)	Damage per day ($)	Total damage ($)	Streamflow (mill. gpd)	Chloride concentration (lb. per mill. gpd)	Damage per day ($)	Total damage ($)
1	1.0									
2	0.5	1.0	1.0	1.0	1.00	1.00	0.5	2.0	2.00	2.00
3	1.5	1.5	1.0	1.5	3.00	4.00	0.5	3.0	6.00	8.00
4	1.0	3.0	2.0	1.5	3.00	7.00	1.0	3.0	6.00	14.00
5	0.5	4.0	2.0	2.0	1.00	8.00	1.0	4.0	2.00	16.00

Damages caused at	Flow Condition I				
	Damage caused by:				Sum of damages caused to
	Plant 1	Plant 2	Plant 3	Plant 4	
Plant 1	$0.00	$0.00	$0.00	$0.00	$0.00
Plant 2	1.00	0.00	0.00	0.00	1.00
Plant 3	2.00	1.00	0.00	0.00	3.00
Plant 4	1.00	0.50	1.50	0.00	3.00
Plant 5	0.25	0.125	0.375	0.25	1.00
Sum of damages caused by:	$4.25	$1.625	$1.875	$0.25	$8.00

Damages caused at	Flow Condition II				
	Damage caused by:				Sum of damages caused to
	Plant 1	Plant 2	Plant 3	Plant 4	
Plant 1	$0.00	$0.00	$0.00	$0.00	$ 0.00
Plant 2	2.00	0.00	0.00	0.00	2.00
Plant 3	4.00	2.00	0.00	0.00	6.00
Plant 4	2.00	1.00	3.00	0.00	6.00
Plant 5	0.50	0.25	0.75	0.50	2.00
Sum of damages caused by:	$8.50	$3.25	$3.75	$0.50	$16.00

stream (say, because a tributary enters), and that the waste it contains is non-degradable (say, chloride). The non-degradability assumption does not change the analysis in any way, but it simplifies the example.

Since damage per day is assumed to be in direct proportion to concentration, a level of charges equal to incremental damage costs can be worked out for each level of flow and for each plant. For example, at flow level one, the charge for plant 1 is $4.25 per unit of waste discharged, which is the sum of the damages caused by plant 1 to plants 2, 3, 4, and 5. This charge is the same regardless of the level of discharge of the other plants. If plant 1 reduced its discharge by half in response to the charge levied on it, its assessment would drop by half to $2.125 —the amount by which downstream damages are reduced.

The manner in which a plant maximizing its profits or minimizing its losses will respond to an effluent charge levied on it at a given level of streamflow and the effect of this response on costs associated with its waste disposal are shown in Figure 5. The plant will, under the circumstances pictured, reduce its waste discharge to point E thus minimizing the costs associated with its waste disposal.

The marginal cost of withholding wastes in an optimal manner includes in the case of salinity such alternatives as temporary lagooning, process adjustments, and cutting back on production. The marginal cost function rises (after some point) because it becomes progressively more expensive to withhold production (say, as inventory is run down), or to adjust production processes. If storage for temporary withholding of wastes is available, the marginal cost function may be a horizontal line until capacity is reached and then become vertical. Since the chart illustrates the situation for a given flow, the cost of using temporary storage capacity now may be the inability to use it at some even lower flow.

When viewed in a long-run, planning sense, the costs of increments of effluent storage capacity may rise if it is necessary to purchase higher-priced land for storage or if the land providing gravity flow to the stream is exhausted and some pumping costs are incurred. The firm acting to minimize its costs (charges plus costs of avoiding them) would continue to use each alternative until $MC_A = MC_B = MC_C = \ldots = MC_N =$ unit charge; in other words, until no further marginal "tradeoffs" are possible which will reduce costs. (In Part III problems of long-run planning are contrasted with short-run problems of adaption with existing capacity.)

To permit the waste-discharging firms to respond rationally to a system of charges, each firm should be furnished with a table relating unit charges to streamflow at the firm's streamflow reference point. In addition, each firm should be supplied with information concerning the

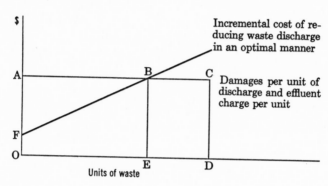

Figure 5.

OD = units of waste discharge if no charge levied on effluent.
OA = damages per unit of waste discharge and effluent charge per unit.
$OACD$ = total damages associated with unrestricted waste discharge, i.e., no effluent charge levied.
OE = reduction of waste discharge with effluent charge OA.
$OFBE$ = total cost of reducing effluent discharge to ED.
$OFBCD$ = total cost associated with waste disposal with ED waste discharge, i.e., residual damage costs plus cost of reducing discharge.
$OABE$ = total damages avoided.
ABF = net reduction in waste disposal associated costs by reducing waste discharge by OE, i.e., $OABE$ minus $OFBE$. This also equals the total cost of *not* reducing the effluent discharge.

probable frequency and duration of various levels of flow.[10] Complexities may arise because the implied assumption that streamflow at various points in the basin rises and falls in strict proportion does not hold precisely in practice. Whether or not such matters should be taken into account would have to be determined in each basin through care-

[10] Or, alternatively, to facilitate long-term planning, the regulatory authority should provide the waste discharger with the "mathematical expectation" of the damages he imposes per unit of discharge. This concept is discussed in Part III.

ful assessment of the significance of such complicating factors as the cost of not dealing with them and the costs involved in more precise adjustment to them.

The relative simplicity of a system of user charges based upon linear damage functions arises from the fact that each waste discharger's damage costs can be determined separately from every other's. This comparative lack of complication may well commend such a system for use even when it is known that the discharge-damage relation is actually somewhat more complex. Here, again, the fact that taking account of greater complexity may rapidly increase costs and yield strongly diminishing returns must be kept in mind in designing an actual system of charges. In other words, among the incremental costs that should not be neglected are the costs of refinements of the system of charges.

The use of linear functions may not be a good approximation of the actual conditions should any of the following situations hold to a significant degree: (1) Damage costs definitely do not increase in direct proportion to the increase in waste concentration; (2) the relationship between different types of wastes is synergistic or cancelling rather than additive; (3) a downstream treatment process removes two or more types of pollutants coming from different sources. In the third case, an inevitable element of arbitrariness is introduced into allocating the costs to individual waste-discharging firms which emit different wastes or the same wastes in different proportions. When the costs of removing residual materials from intake water are strictly "joint" there is literally no non-arbitrary way of determining who is responsible for what. In many cases, however, the costs are probably not truly joint. In these cases, for any given level of concentration the cost of dealing with an increment of the pollutant can be estimated.

In the first two cases the complexity occurs because the cost for which plant 1's discharge can be held responsible becomes in part a function of how much plant 2 discharges.

In order to take non-linear damages into account in the final assessment of costs, it is necessary to establish a fairly detailed, non-linear functional relationship between concentrations and costs for each downstream water user and, if pollutants are not additive in effect, possibly for many combinations of pollutants. An important problem then is how to approximate such functional relationships with data that can be obtained at justifiable expense.[11]

In addition, if either case one or two holds, it is not possible to give the individual discharger as firm advance information concerning what his charges will be at various levels of flow as it is in the simpler situation. It becomes necessary to construct tentative schedules of charges founded on assumptions based on preliminary estimates of discharge at each outfall on the stream. Consequently, great uncertainty attends the actual charges to be imposed.

Given a schedule of charges, however, the firms would tend to develop procedures which fit their individual situations. Some firms may find that user charges are a minor cost and that treatment is comparatively expensive. In this case, the optimum response may be inaction. In other cases, the expected stream user charges may be higher than control measures; a firm may then find it optimal to install treatment or temporary lagooning facilities for use during annual periods of high user charges.[12] For longer-term variations, the best response may sometimes be to curtail production. Properly constructed effluent charges will tend to concentrate waste discharge reduction measures where costs are lowest and/or damages are highest, and such measures will tend to be carried to the point where their incremental cost equals the expected incremental damages avoided.

Hydrologic Variability

The assessment of costs is complicated by the wide fluctuations in streamflow over time. The long-term average discharge of the Delaware River at Trenton, New Jersey, for example, is about 12,000 cfs, while the mean annual low flow drops to roughly one-fourth of this figure and the low flow of record is about one-tenth of the average flow. For the Ruhr, the average flow is about 2,600 cfs, and the average annual

[11] For a discussion of the various sources of direct interaction between waste dischargers, including non-separability, reciprocality, and non-linear damage functions, see Appendix I.

[12] For further discussion of problems involved in the design of optimum abatement measures see chapter 6.

low water flow is only about 140 cfs.[13] These fluctuations cause the dilution and degradation capacities of streams to show strong variation over time, and the concentration of pollutants and attendant damage tend to rise sharply during low stream stages. Oxygen conditions are especially likely to deteriorate radically during such periods because high temperatures (which cause bacteriological activity to increase and the oxygen saturation level of water to decline) ordinarily correspond with low flows. The combination of high concentrations of toxins and low oxygen levels can easily be fatal to fish, and, if oxygen becomes exhausted, extreme nuisance conditions accompany the development of anaerobic processes in a stream. The concentrations of substances which alter the pH value of water, affect its hardness, create tastes and odors, and cause the dissolved solids content to rise, all tend to be higher during periods of low flow. This leads to rising municipal and industrial water supply treatment costs and a variety of damages to facilities and equipment. Thus the social costs of waste disposal show a marked increase during periods of low flow.

From the point of view of resources allocation alone, the varying of effluent charges seasonally to reflect changing social costs has little significance unless the dischargers respond with a variation of waste loads.

There are a number of ways in which industrial plants and municipalities can substantially adjust waste loads entering a stream over short periods of time. Treatment processes can be designed and operated to yield varying levels of treatment of wastes, although very high levels will be achievable only at rapidly rising incremental costs. Some manufacturers may find it worthwhile to withhold wastes for some period of time, especially in nonurban areas where detention ponds could be built without a great expenditure on land.[14]

Manufacturers can also make process and production adjustments in response to variable effluent charges. The lowest cost solution for some

[13] Delaware figure from *Surface Water Supply of the United States 1956; Part I-B North Atlantic Slope Basins, New York to York River*, Geological Survey Water Supply Paper 1432 (Washington: U.S. Government Printing Office, 1959). The Ruhr flows figures are from Helmut Moehle, "Wasserwirtschaftliche Probleme an Industriefluessen" (Problems of Water Management on Industrial Streams), *Die Wasserwirtschaft*, Vol. 45, 1954.

[14] See the discussion of this alternative in chapter 2.

firms, especially those making storable goods, might be to cut back on production during low flow periods, perhaps by planning vacation schedules to coincide with typical periods of low flow and highest temperatures. In this way the goods are stored, rather than the waste water or the receiving stream.

The amount of pretreatment might also be varied by neutralizing acids and by handling certain types of concentrated wastes separately and not using water for their disposal. Many other adjustments are probably feasible and might be optimal.

Streamflow forecasting and advance notice of levels of charges to manufacturers would be necessary to permit the waste discharger to respond optimally to changing streamflow and damage conditions.

One of the merits of charges is that they force some of the most complex decisions onto the individual firms. One manufacturer, for example, may be able to lower his costs by varying the quantity and/or quality of his waste discharges over time so as to avoid peak effluent charges. Another manufacturer may be in an entirely different situation. Aggregate costs can be lowered by permitting each manufacturer to respond in accordance with the cost conditions confronting him. An administrative authority would seldom be in a position to make such a decision.

Because variations in water flow cause the costs associated with waste disposal to vary through time, it is reasonable, and from the point of view of optimal resources allocation, essential, that prices charged polluters also vary through time, if the costs of administering such a system are not excessive.

A system of effluent charges that vary with streamflow would closely resemble the peak pricing method so widely used by electrical utilities. Under this method, the price of the service performed varies with the load on the system. In the case of electrical utilities, price varies by time of day and by season. Some large electrical utility systems have instituted very detailed differentiation of rates in implementing peak load pricing.[15] In the case of water quality control probably no more than seasonal variations could be justified.

[15] See Thomas Marschak, "Capital Budgeting and Pricing in the French Nationalized Industries," *The Journal of Business*, April, 1960, p. 133. Jack Hirshleifer, James C. DeHaven, and Jerome W. Milliman, *Water Supply—Economics, Technology and Policy* (Chicago: University of Chicago Press, 1960), ch. V. For

In assessing the merits of applying peak load pricing principles to effluent discharges, the costs of determining variation in the quality and quantity of effluent over the relevant period must of course be considered. In the Ruhr area of Germany, the only area where basin-wide effluent charges are assessed, the quantity and quality of effluent are sampled once or twice a year.

The costs of operating an analysis and sampling program using standard laboratory methods would mount sharply if an effort were made to determine quality and quantity variation with sufficient continuity to permit peak load pricing. The burden of proof might be put on the manufacturers themselves, but this would not necessarily lower the social cost of a monitoring program and might well increase it.

Fortunately, in recent years, progress has been made in the development of automatic monitoring devices. Such variables of river quality as dissolved oxygen, acidity-alkalinity, salinity, specific conductance (dissolved solids), temperature, and turbidity can be continuously measured with fairly simple devices.[16] Some measurements are already

recent theoretical discussion of peak load pricing with special reference to investment decisions, see M. Boiteux, "Peakload Pricing," *The Journal of Business,* April, 1960, p. 157; and P. O. Steiner, "Peak Loads and Efficient Pricing," *Quarterly Journal of Economics,* November, 1957, p. 585; and Jack Hirshleifer, "Peak Loads and Efficient Pricing: Comment," *Quarterly Journal of Economics,* 1958, p. 460.

[16] Some of the most advanced work on automatic monitoring systems has been done by the Ohio River Sanitation Commission (Cincinnati, Ohio). See the ORSANCO annual reports. The most comprehensive discussions known to the author of the instruments and techniques used by ORSANCO is found in Edward J. Cleary, "Ein Fluss-Roboter fuer die Kontrolle der Wasserguete" (A Stream Robot for the Control of Water Quality), *Die Wasserwirtschaft,* Heft 4, April, 1961, p. 85. Some major reports on German experience with automatic monitoring devices are W. Husman, "Einsatz neuerer Messmethoden auf dem Gebiet der Abwasserreinigung and Gewaesserkontrolle im Bereich der Emschergenossenschaft und des Lippeverbandes" (Institution of Newer Measuring Methods in the Field of Effluent Treatment and Water Control in the Area of the Emschergenossenschaft and the Lippeverband), *Schweizerische Zeitschrift fuer Hydrologie,* Vol. 22, 1960, p. 461. W. Husman, "Mess- und Regelanlagen zur Gewaesserueberwachung" (Measurement and Regulation Devices for Water Monitoring), *Wasser und Boden,* Vol. 6, 1961, p. 181. R. Schuh, "Messgeraete fuer die Untersuchung und Ueberwachung von Fluss- und Abwasser" (Measurement Devices for the Investigation and Monitoring of Stream Water and Effluents), *Die Wasserwirtschaft,* September, 1958, p. 315. W. Husman and G. Stracke, "Kontinuierliche Sauerstoffmessung in Fluss- und Abwaessern" (Continuous Measurement of Oxygen in Stream Water and Effluents), *Die Wasserwirtschaft,* October, 1957, p. 13.

successfully carried out on effluents and there is considerable promise that others can be developed. Optimism appears justified that accurate and comparatively simple devices for continuous measurement of a wide variety of water quality characteristics can be worked out.

In some instances a thorough laboratory test may be necessary to establish relations that will permit certain characteristics readily measured with automatic devices to be used as surrogates for those that are expensive or impossible to measure. For example, it may be possible to establish a relation between certain measurable characteristics of an effluent and fish kills, which can substitute for a direct toxicity test.

It is probably not excessively visionary to foresee a time in the relatively near future when a number of important quality parameters can be continuously recorded at a central point for every major outfall in an entire basin at comparatively modest cost.[17]

The administrative problems and costs of such a program should be considerably more manageable than the several schemes which have been seriously proposed to register the passage of specific automobiles, over specific routes, at specific times as a foundation for the application of peak load pricing to automobile traffic.[18]

SPECIAL PROBLEMS IN COST MEASUREMENT

Up to this point the costs associated with waste disposal have been broadly classified as damage costs and abatement costs and discussed in general terms. In this section, attention is centered on three specific kinds of damage costs that are particularly difficult to measure—those relating to aesthetics, recreation, and domestic water supply. Many other costs, though they offer difficulties, are, in principle, rather

[17] See Cleary, *op. cit.*, p. 89. It may be noted that there are parallels to this in terms of telemetering data from rain and snow gauges, and the monitoring at various points in a power system for the purpose of economic dispatching.

[18] See for example, A. A. Walters, "The Theory and Measurement of Private and Social Costs of Highway Travel," *Econometrica*, October, 1961, p. 676, where the "milometer" is proposed; and William S. Vickrey, "General and Specific Financing of Urban Services," in *Public Expenditure Decisions in the Urban Community* (Washington, D.C.: Resources for the Future, Inc., 1963). General Precision Systems of Aylesbury, England, has proposed a meter mounted on the vehicle that would be actuated by signals received from electric cables in the road; see *The Economist*, October 19, 1963, p. 305.

straightforwardly measurable, and attempts are being made to quantify some of them.[19] A study of municipal water treatment costs is under way, for example, and Resources for the Future is supporting several industry studies which are aimed at developing methods for estimating the costs imposed by quality deterioration, as well as actually making estimates.

Before an explicit discussion of the special problems of recreation, aesthetics, and domestic water supply, it should be noted that these uses are not affected by *every* water quality problem. Salinity, for example, does not appear to involve the question of health, aesthetics, or recreation to any significant degree (see chapter 5, which deals with salinity as a particular waste problem on the Ohio River).

Aesthetics and Recreation

The destructive effects of water pollution on the general environment are unfortunately obvious. Obnoxious odors of septic sewage may carry for miles; untreated municipal sewage contains floating and suspended materials that destroy the beauty of the water; and industrial effluents may render the water unattractive by coloring it. Fortunately, extreme nuisance is unlikely to occur in a stream which is used for multiple purposes and where a system of charges causes the costs of various other uses to be considered in water quality control decisions. Where it is necessary to evaluate aesthetic nuisance, however, the problem is very great.

Individuals in a community participate in the benefits provided by the aesthetic qualities of nearby bodies of water whether they help meet the costs of providing and maintaining them or not. There is, therefore, no incentive for an individual to express his true preferences, and a market cannot develop for the control of the general environmental effects of pollution. Not only is it impossible for the market to effectively represent preferences for pollution control, but there is no way of parceling out and selling goods of this kind. For the same reasons, litigation by private parties will not adequately represent

[19] Some of the complexities of measuring costs are discussed in Allen V. Kneese, *Water Pollution: Economic Aspects and Research Needs* (Washington, D.C.: Resources for the Future, Inc., 1962).

such preferences either. In the absence of usable evaluations, a judgment that extreme aesthetic nuisance is to be avoided, at least in heavily developed areas, must find almost universal consensus. Minimum standards imposed, for example, to prevent the discharge of obnoxious floating materials, may be a simple and satisfactory method of handling one aspect of this problem.

There are possibilities for evaluation, however. The aesthetic damages occurring in a river which does not cause extreme nuisance are pretty well limited to those who own nearby property and those who would come from some distance to enjoy the river. Methods have been proposed and are under development to assess the value of advantages resulting to these classes of users when they are beneficiaries of recreation development. The procedure is to impute a demand curve from the implicit valuation of the users who travel to the site and from the enhancement of property values.[20] Such a procedure may have promise as a means of gauging recreation effects where beneficiaries can be reasonably well identified. Where a pollutant affects both recreation and aesthetics (which except in cases of extreme nuisance may be viewed as almost joint products), a measure of this kind might yield a package value for both.[21] Methods of estimating willingness to pay using questionnaires are also being explored.[22] Econometric methods may be applied to these evaluation procedures to project the recreation and aesthetic values which would result from the alleviation of extreme pollution conditions.

Although it is not yet possible to assign specific values to aesthetics and recreation that will permit a precise imposition of charges on polluters, there appears to be considerable hope for achieving fairly satisfactory and detailed evaluation of aesthetic and recreational effects within the ranges necessary for most applications. In the meantime, it is possible to check the reasonableness of some of the *implied* values.

[20] See Jack Knetsch, "Outdoor Recreation Demands and Benefits," *Land Economics*, November, 1963.

[21] There are, however, serious deficiencies in a property value measure as the sole and full measure of benefits from pollution control. See Kneese, *op. cit.*, p. 44.

[22] Robert K. Davis, "The Economics of Recreational Development in the Maine Woods" (Ph.D. Thesis, Harvard University, 1963). A questionnaire procedure is also being used by William G. Brown and Emery Castle, Department of Economics, Oregon State University.

Public Health and Domestic Water Supplies

Some of the most difficult evaluation problems arise in connection with drinking water. Damages to other household uses are, in principle, subject to fairly straightforward evaluation. While no careful, detailed, and comprehensive studies have been made of the costs imposed on domestic use by various pollutants over a range of concentrations, such studies present no unusually difficult conceptual problems and should be promptly carried out. Almost all destructive pollutants in raw water supplies are treatable over a range of costs which may make water supply treatment competitive with waste treatment in certain situations. (Chlorides are perhaps the major exception.) Moreover, there are often three or four courses of action to be considered even after the water is withdrawn from the raw water source: (1) treatment at the water plant, (2) treatment by the consumer (as in home water softeners), (3) a shift by the consumer to alternative sources (distilled water for irons), (4) acceptance of the actual physical damages (corrosion, excess soap use, etc.). Study should be able to suggest the combinations of alternatives that will minimize costs for a variety of quality variables and their concentrations. The incremental cost of such combinations must be weighed off against the costs of withholding various degrees of the polluting substances from the raw water supply

Public health presents difficulties analogous to those described in the section on technological external economies, except that in this case the interdependencies are between consumers rather than producers. Infectious disease carries possibilities of direct effects on others that are not taken into account in individual decisions to avoid disease. Consequently, society may wish to impose health standards higher than those a substantial segment of the population would freely choose to buy.

Some of the effects of illness upon over-all income can be measured.[23] In certain situations an increment in national product (re-

[23] See Burton A. Weisbrod, *Economics of Public Health, Measuring the Economic Impact of Diseases* (Philadelphia: University of Pennsylvania Press, 1961). See also Edwin E. and Peter P. Rogers, "On Estimating Benefit-Cost Ratios for

duced real cost associated with waste disposal) could easily justify the installation of water treatment facilities. Thus, some degree of water treatment—primarily chlorination—can surely be justified solely on economic grounds. The debilitating effect of typhoid, cholera, and dysentery, as well as the resources consumed in treating these diseases, could easily involve high social costs.

However, the urban population of the United States has chosen to set standards of water treatment that are designed to eliminate any substantial possibility of epidemic. Cases of infectious disease resulting from water withdrawn from public water supply systems using modern treatment methods are practically unknown. The few that can definitely be traced to water supplies are the results of breakdown, or of improper operation. Present bacteriological public water supply standards reflect an attitude toward disease that is not based upon the maximization of economic return.

Thus, accepting for the moment some prevailing standard for water supply delivered to the consumer, is it necessary to establish *stream* standards to support the water supply standard? If so, what should they be? Presuming that public health aspects of bathing are reflected in the evaluation of recreation and that other activities involving contact with raw water can be neglected, the sole economic problem is to determine the lowest cost method of achieving desired water quality at the tap. This might or might not involve sewage treatment and chlorination of sewage effluent. Since coliform bacteria die off rather quickly in a body of water and since all waters—even those heavily loaded with pollutants—have some self-purification powers, simple cost minimization would probably favor water supply treatment over sewage treatment. Biological treatment may be necessary for unassimilated wastes in highly dilute form. This presents some difficulties, but its cost can be calculated, as can the costs of the extra equipment and manpower needed to protect against system failures. Assume that these water supply treatment procedures are the best alternatives to higher water quality in the existing source and their costs are levied on the waste dischargers. If these costs are substan-

Water Supply Investments," *American Journal of Public Health,* October, 1962, pp. 1729ff.; and Selma Mushkin, "Health as an Investment," *Journal of Political Economy,* 1962, p. 129.

tially higher than waste treatment above certain concentrations of residual waste material, induced waste treatment will keep these levels from being reached.

Bacteriological contamination, the classic public health consideration, is in some respects simpler to define and deal with than the health problems presented by some other pollutants. Standard inorganic poisons and a limited range of highly toxic organic materials have been studied for some time by U.S. Public Health authorities, and tolerance levels have been set. These tolerances are based primarily on acute toxicity tests and large safety margins. Even with respect to the standard poisons there is considerable doubt about the specific character of chronic effects, and more study and better tests are needed. Nevertheless, the existing standards must be accepted for the present. These poisons can be removed from public supplies by treatment, which may have to be by distillation. If this is the alternative to removal at the source, its cost provides a basis for levying a charge on effluents.

More intractable difficulties are posed by the synthetic organic chemicals produced by modern industry. Over 500,000 have been synthesized, and a substantial and variable number are found in low concentration in waters used as a source of public drinking water supplies.[24] Standard water supply treatment methods often have little effect on them. The possibility that these chemicals, even in very low concentration, may be harmful is of concern to public health authorities. The presence of toxic materials is particularly significant in water, because total human ingestion of water far exceeds that of all solids. The task of determining the effects of all, or even a substantial portion, of these compounds is impossibly large under current circumstances. It has been estimated that fewer than 100 qualified toxicologists are now working in the United States.[25] The scarcity of qualified personnel plus the complexity of tracing chronic and possible genetic effects of chemical compounds on mammals, means that

[24] See M. B. Ettinger, "Proposed Toxicity Screening Procedures for Use in Protecting Drinking Water Quality," *Journal American Water Works Association,* Vol. 52, No. 6, June, 1960.

[25] B. B. Berger, U.S. Public Health Service, Robert A. Taft Sanitary Engineering Center, Cincinnati, in conversation with the author.

the cost of testing a single compound is very high. Estimates running from $50,000 to $500,000 per compound have been reported by manufacturers required to demonstrate the safety of food additives and drugs.[26] In addition, it is not enough to test chemicals on a "one at a time" basis under laboratory conditions, since the toxicity of a particular compound may be altered by the action of other chemicals or bacteria in the water. Transformations of an analogous character have occurred outside water bodies. In the cranberry episode of 1960, for example, the oxide of the herbicide heptachlore turned out to be more toxic than the compound itself. In addition, the destructive effects of toxic chemicals ingested in combination apparently are ordinarily additive, but in some instances synergistic or opposing.[27] There appears to be little immediate hope of obtaining reasonable tolerance standards for long-term ingestion of each of the many hundreds of toxic organic substances which, at least periodically, exist in waters drawn upon for public supplies. Even if such standards could be elaborated, testing for each substance would be an impossible burden for water utilities and/or a regional water authority.

A simple index such as the coliform count used to measure the presence of pathogens may be workable for organic chemicals.[28] This technique is based upon the amount (in parts per billion) of organic materials that can be eluted from a carbon filter by repeated extractions with chloroform. Public water supplies in the United States rarely require special treatment to meet the U.S. Public Health Service recommended limit of 200 ppb in finished water supplies. (Higher levels of concentration are usually associated with taste and odor problems.) Theoretically, a limit based upon a composite measurement has many drawbacks, but the proposed aggregate standard provides a value which can at least provisionally be accepted as a drinking water standard. Some techniques, short of distillation, for reduc-

[26] *Wall Street Journal*, February 10, 1961, p. 1. While these reported estimates may be exaggerated, the lower figure was also quoted to the author by Bernard B. Berger as an approximate minimum cost for testing the chronic toxicity of a single compound in water.

[27] Herbert E. Stokinger and Richard L. Woodward, "Toxicological Methods for Establishing Drinking Water Standards," *Journal American Water Works Association*, Vol. 50, No. 4, April, 1958, p. 528.

[28] M. B. Ettinger, *op. cit.*

ing the quantity of chloroform extractables are available to the utility operator. Activated carbon is particularly effective against the organic chemicals. Again, a basis is established for the assessment of costs.

EFFICIENT QUALITY CONTROL
WHEN QUALITY "STANDARDS" ARE IMPOSED

The discussion of measurement problems in this chapter has introduced complications beyond those of the *comparatively* simple situation when waste disposal costs (damage costs and abatement costs) are rather straightforwardly measurable. It was indicated that procedures could probably be worked out to provide acceptable approximations of aesthetic and recreation values, but it appeared that public health considerations would have to be represented by some sort of standards. However, the cost of the next best alternative to high raw water quality from a given source can be calculated, and this can serve as the basis for appropriate effluent charges or abatement subsidies. This might be, for example, the cost of treatment to meet the standard, the cost of going to an alternative source for all domestic water or for drinking water only.

This cost can be treated *as though it were a damage cost* although it does not conform to the earlier definition where *damage costs* were tied directly to consumer valuations and could be treated as "social costs" in the same sense that *abatement costs* are "social costs," i.e., measurable in terms of the consumer satisfactions from alternative uses of resources. Damage costs arising from standards are not tied to consumer valuations by such a direct means. They are best viewed as arising from a political or administrative restriction on the minimization of costs associated with waste disposal.

Once a given set of standards for drinking water is established, the costs of meeting them by the best means at the point of use should be treated as damage costs in assessing charges or determining subsidies. The reasoning justifying this statement is straightforward. If the standards are really to be met, the economic question becomes one of meeting them with the least resource cost. After determining how to meet the standards at minimum cost at the point of use, the problem is to induce an optimum quality of raw water and optimum measures for producing it. If, for example, it costs more to meet the standard at the point of use than at the upstream point of origin, and if this opportunity cost is reflected in the decisions of upstream dischargers, they will treat their wastes. The result will tend to be a combination of measures which meets the "standard" at minimum cost. While the surrogate measure of downstream costs is not a complete substitute for "damage" evaluation, it permits a wider range of alternatives to be weighed off against one another than if a *stream* standard is imposed, and therefore a closer approximation to the optimum.

The situation is somewhat simpler, however, if a standard is imposed for water in the watercourse. One form such a standard could take is to set an upper limit on the concentration of a given pollutant (say a material toxic to fish). Given the assumptions concerning the character of the stream and the opportunities available for handling water quality problems, a system of charges or subsidies can be established which provides incentives for achieving this objective at lowest cost. (This situation is discussed in detail in chapter 5.) The following general statements are of significance here:

1. If a standard is set for a critical point on a stream and discharge of a given waste must be cut back to achieve the standard, a charge (or subsidy) per unit of non-degradable waste discharge can be worked out which will achieve the standard. The same is true of degradable wastes, but in this case the charge will depend upon the degree to which the wastes are degraded in the stream between the outfall and the critical point. From the viewpoint of this study, credit must be given for degradation in the stream—not because it is equitable—for no criteria of equity are offered—but because it is necessary for the minimization of costs. To see this, imagine the extreme case where a waste is fully degraded before it reaches the critical point in the stream. If a charge were imposed on the quality at the outfall, abatement outlays would be induced unnecessarily. The methods of forecasting concentrations in long sections of stream, described in chapter 2 would be valuable here.

2. The effluent charges procedure would have the advantage over other possible techniques (see chapter 5) of permitting each polluter to adjust in the best way for his particular circumstances. Individual

dischargers could withhold wastes in storage lagoons, adjust production processes, treat wastes, cut back on production, change the character of their output, pay the charge, or use a combination of these and other relevant procedures. It can be shown (again see chapter 5) that an appropriate charge would tend to minimize the cost of achieving the standard by inducing equalization of incremental costs for the various alternatives and for the same alternative at different locations.[29]

3. The charge (payment) required to achieve the standard indicates the incremental cost of achieving the standard. This means that without specific knowledge of the nature or the relative costs of the alternatives available to upstream dischargers, the responsible authority can estimate the marginal social cost of the standard.[30] This is important for judging the appropriateness of the standard. Presume, for example, that the standard relates to the killing of fish by, say, a toxic substance, and that it is not possible to establish the value of the "damage costs" of varying concentrations of the pollutant. The charges necessary to achieve the standard give an indication of what a small change in the standards and their accompanying physical effects *must at least be worth.* For example, if the charge is $1.00

[29] It may be appropriate here to explain the reasoning which underlies the proposition that a payment for reducing waste discharge could accomplish the same thing in the "standards" case. Assume a non-degradable waste and a standard which is to be enforced at a certain critical point. Assume that an authority stands ready to pay an amount per unit of waste kept out of the stream just large enough to achieve the standard. Since the point of origin of the waste is immaterial this fee will be uniform for each discharger (see chapter 5). If a discharger has a method of abating his discharge which costs (over a certain range) less than the value of the payment, he will use it if he is trying to maximize his profits and he will use it until the cost of the last increment of use equals the payment. On the other hand, he will not use any procedure which costs more than the payment, because it is less costly to forego the payment. Consequently the same marginal equalities will hold as if a charge had been levied. As previously stated, the proviso must be made that the payment will be made to a discharger even if his best alternative is going out of business.

[30] It may be noted that this value, which represents the cost or saving produced by a small alteration in the standard, is precisely analogous to the information yielded by "duals" of linear programming problems when constraints are imposed on the objective function. If, for example, instead of the decentralized decision-making approach outlined here, the cost-minimizing "solution" had been obtained by means of an exceedingly complex linear programming model that requires vast amounts of information, the dual would have provided an estimate of the marginal cost of the "standard."

per unit of waste, a slight reduction in the standard must cause at least $1.00 worth of damage costs per unit if the standard is worth maintaining. This type of information facilitates a decision on whether to raise or lower standards.

COMPLEMENTARITIES IN TREATMENT OR OTHER MEASURES FOR ABATEMENT OF WASTE DISCHARGES

A thoroughgoing system in a basin with reasonably complex development would probably result in a whole array of charges. Some of these would actually represent downstream damage costs. Others might relate to some aggregate type of measure like chloroform extractables.

Abatement measures to reduce one pollutant at a point of discharge may simultaneously reduce others. Standard biological treatment, for example, not only removes the degradable organics, but has some effect on persistent organics such as alkyl benzene sulfonate (the active ingredient of most synthetic detergents), plant nutrients, bacteria, and other substances.

Since joint costs cannot be allocated in a way that assists rational decisions, the discharger endeavoring to minimize his waste disposal costs would have to calculate the amount by which the joint effect of his action would reduce his charges, and weigh it against his specific cost of introducing and operating abatement measures. In a system of charges designed both to reflect downstream costs and fulfill the established "standards," the level of charges needed to accomplish the "standards" could still be established in the manner outlined above. For example, if it is found that a charge can be reduced without having water quality drop below the level specified in the standard, this means that (1) the charge is too high in terms of those dischargers responding directly to it, and/or (2) pollutant A is jointly treated with pollutant B by at least some dischargers and the charge levied on B is high enough to produce lower than necessary levels of A.

The charge levied on A would then be reduced until the standard is just met; if the influence of joint treatment is strong, the charge might be dropped to zero. However, a point may be reached where the amount of A does not respond to a lowering of charges. This could be because some plants which discharge only A reduce abatement activity or because the mix of pollutants is such that the reduced charge on A lowers the incentive to abatement by its effect on the value of the total charge for the substances jointly removed. In either case, the charge which just meets the standard reflects the cost of an incremental change in the standard.

An "ideal" system of charges would reflect the costs imposed downstream, and all charges levied to meet the standard would be at the lowest level consistent with the standard.

EFFLUENT STANDARDS

Consideration of *effluent* standards, perhaps the most discussed method of achieving some co-ordination between the water quality desired in rivers and individual waste discharges, has been purposely postponed until now so that the problem of external economies could be examined first in terms of charges and payments. These measures are the ones that have been traditionally advocated by economists for dealing with externalities; they are also consistent with the operation of payments mechanisms in private markets.

In this section effluent standards are compared with a system of charges and payments as a means of achieving water quality management. A first and basic point is that *if a regional authority had full information concerning the costs associated with waste disposal, it could establish a set of effluent standards that would have the same effect on resource allocation as an ideal system of charges.* A charge on each individual outfall tends to produce a certain quality of effluent. Standards could be set to obtain the same effluent quality at each outfall.[31] It is important to note, however, that such a standard would have to be stated in terms of amount of wastes discharged (pounds, tons, etc.) rather than in terms of the traditional concentrations. In order to impose such effluent standards, it would be necessary to forecast the response of each discharger at each level of flow to a system of charges which reflected the damage costs and point-of-use

[31] The assumption of no negotiations between private parties is necessary here.

standards in the area. This would mean a whole system of individually tailored effluent standards which varied with flow. Minimization of the sum of abatement and damage costs *could* be achieved by this system as well as by an ideal system of charges or subsidies. Neither can claim an advantage on the basis of superior performance under *ideal* conditions of information and authority on the part of a responsible regional agency. The differences leading to preference of one or another are in the area of administrative ease or difficulty and income distribution or equity.[32]

Providing the objective of each system is the minimization of the costs associated with waste disposal, the claim can be made for a system of charges that under some circumstances—which probably include numerous actual cases—it requires less information to approximate the objective. This is true where a specified standard of stream water quality is set, and where charges reflect damage costs and the costs are approximately linear functions of concentration for individual pollutants and approximately additive for different pollutants. In this case, charges based upon damage costs will tend toward a minimization of damage and abatement costs as explained in some detail earlier. This result follows even though abatement costs are not explicitly known.

It was also previously indicated that, by a series of approximations, a charge can be set that will achieve a specified stream standard and that will tend to produce the equi-marginal costs for alternatives which are necessary for cost minimization. Sample studies could produce a forecast of the appropriate level of charges suitable for planning purposes. Since land values, production processes, and other significant variables differ from case to case, specific information concerning "marginal tradeoffs" between alternative abatement procedures at different outfalls would be necessary to establish cost-minimizing combinations by the use of effluent standards.

It may be argued that "equity" demands that the *standards at each outfall be the same.* It is not at all clear, however, that it is more

---

[32] In the case of industry, long-term impacts on location decisions and on the decision whether or not to produce can be different if a standard is levied to equate marginal abatement costs and marginal damage costs than if an ideal system of charges or subsidies is developed. See discussion of ideal charges and subsidies in Appendix II. In most instances this effect will probably be minor.

equitable to impose the *same standard* on all dischargers regardless of the *differences* in *costs* of meeting it than it is to impose the *same charge* on each unit of waste discharged or pay the *same* subsidy for each unit kept out. None of these procedures has the same economic impact on each individual firm. The merit of the charges and payments is that the differences make sense in terms of minimum resources use to achieve a given end. If the income distributive result is considered inequitable, a system of direct payments can, *at least in principle,* be worked out which will achieve almost any income distributive effects which may be desired.

Where actual conditions depart importantly from the stated conditions, which greatly simplify the problem of imposing charges, detailed information on specific alternatives at each outfall and their related marginal costs are needed for forecasting and later establishing both appropriate effluent charges and effluent standards. In fact, if there is substantial direct interaction between waste dischargers, implementing either system becomes very complex, and precisely optimal results may not be attainable, even in principle, because of uncertainty. In this instance, reasonable rules of thumb will have to be developed for the regulation of individual waste discharge.[33]

The charges alternative still seems to have certain advantages although these are harder to specify than in the previous cases. For example, a charge offers some incentive to take action even to the lowest level of waste discharge, while a standard (even though stated in terms of quantity rather than concentration) provides no incentive to curb waste discharge beyond the required level even though it might be possible to do so quite inexpensively. Stating this another way, given that the optimum quality of stream water is missed by a given amount, one may hypothesize that the effluent standards procedure will tend to involve the greater resources use. Or to put it still another way, for any given level of information, the charges alternative would appear to involve less resources cost, since charges automatically tend toward an equalization of marginal costs.

If the complexities in an actual situation result in the specification of a stream standard rather than an actual effort to assess and distribute damage costs, the advantages of the charges procedure be-

[33] See Appendix I.

come those already described. And for any given degree of approximation of optimum results, the information or administrative requirements for charges are no greater than for effluent standards. For example, if the burden of proof concerning the quality of effluents is put on the discharger for one, it can be for the other. Charges have the additional advantage of providing funds for the implementation of measures of regional scope.

The sometimes stated proposition that effluent standards should be based upon the stream and its uses can be given a quite specific meaning within the social cost framework here elaborated. However, for a variety of approximations to procedures for minimizing social costs it appears that charges can accomplish water quality management objectives more efficiently than can standards.

APPENDIX TO CHAPTER 4

I. "Separable" and "Inseparable" External Diseconomies

Recently a significant distinction between separable and inseparable externalities has been made in an article by Davis and Whinston.[1] The separability case requires that the marginal cost of each firm linked to another by a technological externality be given entirely in terms of its own output variable. In essence this means that the externality affects only total costs, not marginal (incremental) costs. This would follow, for example, if construction of factory A cuts off the breeze from factory B and makes it necessary to install central air conditioning in the latter. The new total cost function becomes a vertical displacement of the old, and marginal costs are not changed, as is shown in the following example.

Since marginal costs of one firm are not changed by the output decisions of the other firm, the externality does not cause output to be different from what it would have been in the absence of the externality

[1] Otto A. Davis and Andrew H. Whinston, "Externalities, Welfare, and the Theory of Games," *Journal of Political Economy*, June, 1962, pp. 241ff. For an excellent brief article relating Davis and Whinston to the previously cited articles by Coase and Buchanan and Stubblebine, see Ralph Turvey, "On Divergences between Social Cost and Private Cost," *Economica*, August, 1963, p. 309.

presuming it continues to be in the affected firm's interest to produce at all. The effect of the externality is intra-marginal and thus merely affects the firm's profit position and the decision whether to continue production or to stop.

Plant B output	Total cost before factory A	Marginal cost	Total cost after factory A	Marginal cost
1	1.0		2.0	
		1.5		1.5
2	2.5		3.5	
		2.0		2.0
3	4.5		5.5	

A non-separable externality is defined to occur when the *marginal* cost in a productive process is affected by the level of output in another process. As the authors indicate, "the difference between the separable and the non-separable cases lies in the fact that externality enters the cost function in a multiplicative manner rather than in a strictly additive way. The effect of this is that, for the non-separable case, marginal cost is not an unambiguous function of the firm's own output." [2] For example, assume that a petroleum refining plant A, which expels a hot effluent, locates upstream from a petroleum refining plant B, which is operated by a different firm and which uses the stream for cooling water. For simplicity assume that recirculation in the plant or precooling of water before discharge or intake is not possible. Cooling efficiency for plant B will drop, and it will have to pump more water for cooling per unit of output. The marginal costs of plant B will be affected by the externality. An example is shown below.

Plant B output	Total pumping costs before Plant A	Marginal cost	Total pumping costs after Plant A	Marginal cost
1	1.0		2.0	
		1.5		3.0
2	2.5		5.0	
		2.0		4.0
3	4.5		9.0	

Interaction is created between the decision-making efforts of the individual firms, since plant B cannot determine its most profitable level of output without knowing the level of output of plant A.

[2] Davis and Whinston, *op. cit.*, p. 253.

However, even in this instance of non-separability, a particular marginal cost function for plant B corresponds to each level of output of plant A. Plant A can determine its own profit-maximizing level of output, and at this rate of production a specific level of output will also maximize profits for plant B (although these will in general not be the levels of output which will maximize joint profits for both plants taken together). In principle, however, a stable equilibrium output will arise, and it is possible to compute the amount of a levy on the output of plant A which will maximize joint profits. The appropriate level of charge will be the one which causes the marginal net loss imposed on firm B to be considered an opportunity cost in firm A. Thus, despite an implication which could easily be read into the Davis-Whinston article, non-separability as such does not necessarily mean that an appropriate charge cannot in principle be levied. However, in the case of water pollution, non-separability does cause considerable difficulties in the assessment of effluent charges. Two factors account for this: (1) In some realistic situations the waste disposal associated damages take a "reciprocal" form; and (2) even in cases where externalities are not reciprocal, considerable complexity occurs in the assessment of charges if successive waste disposers and water users impose damages on each other seriatim.

The reciprocal case occurs, for example, when plant A expels a polluting substance which varies with output and increases the costs of preparing water for use in plant B. Plant B carries on a production process which creates a variable noise level depending upon output and which raises the costs of plant A by, say, increasing the proportion of output which is defective. Assuming that the aspects of production affected by the reciprocal externality are significantly large, neither plant's marginal cost function is given independently of the other's. It is to such an instance that the following comment by Davis and Whinston is relevant, "We have here, even in what is usually considered the certain world of competitive price theory, an example in which decisions must be made under uncertainty. It is this aspect of the externality problem which is roughly analogous to duopoly theory." Under these circumstances the determinate equilibrium is replaced by mutual interdependence giving rise to individual and unpredictable strategies on the part of the firm. In this case the response of the individual firms to levies or subsidies would also tend to be unpredictable. Moreover, even providing any individual waste-discharging firm with a schedule of charges would be an extremely complex undertaking since it would be necessary to anticipate each possible level of output of the other firm.

Reciprocal non-separable externalities are the ones most likely to lead to a merger, since neither firm can maximize its own profit position without reference to the other.

When discharge takes place into ponds, lakes, or estuaries, the external diseconomies will tend to be of a reciprocal variety, and, in principle, a precise, determinate solution may be arrived at only by an integrated decision unit.

In flowing streams the externalities created by waste disposal are separable and non-separable diseconomies of the non-reciprocal variety, since the discharged wastes are carried downstream. Accordingly, at least in the two-party case where the upstream party simply has a physically superior position, there is in principle no reason why an optimizing charge cannot be laid upon the waste discharger. Even in a stream, however, non-separability causes problems in the assessment of charges, especially when there are a number of water users and waste dischargers, because the optimal charge becomes a function of the output level of the affected parties.

Assume an initial equilibrium along a stream where a number of water users and waste dischargers impose external diseconomies on one another seriatim. Assume the regulatory authority starts by imposing the incremental costs of the last one of these (Z) upon the previous one (Y) and so on back up the line. When the charge is levied upon Y the outputs of both Y and Z change. As the cost imposed by X on Y is levied on X the optimal output of Y changes again and accordingly so does that of Z. We have an interdependent system, and a simultaneous solution is necessary for the entire system. Not only is the problem analytically complex, but it would require detailed information on the costs of reducing waste discharge as well as damages imposed, and it might not be possible to devise a combination of charges that would achieve the necessary simultaneous adjustment. Each time there was an exogenous change in output in one firm the entire system would have to be recalculated.

Things may not be so dark, however. For one thing, municipal waste loads are not sensitive to damage costs imposed upon the municipality,[3] and thus do not give rise to serial effects. Recreation, one of the major uses affected by quality deterioration, does not itself produce a signifi-

---

[3] They are of course sensitive to charges assessed upon the municipality's waste discharge.

cant waste load. Moreover, some industrial damages such as corrosion appear to be separable. In other instances, effects on marginal costs may usually be too small to affect output appreciably.

Obviously, empirical work is urgently needed to determine how damages occur and whether they are separable or non-separable, and to quantify them. Some of this is now under way under RFF sponsorship.

Let us proceed under the assumption that separability is a reasonably good approximation of actual externalities related to waste disposal. Unfortunately, separability does not eliminate the problem of direct interaction between waste disposers.

A problem of interaction analogous to that associated with reciprocal externalities may result when multiple waste discharges affect the same user or users. The essential nature of this problem can perhaps best be depicted by a simple example. Assume that two waste dischargers directly across a stream from one another discharge the same type of waste. They do not impose external diseconomies on one another, but both of them impose diseconomies on a third party downstream. If the function relating damages to concentration is linear, the incremental damages associated with successive units of waste discharge are constant and the problem is comparatively simple. In this instance, the waste discharges are essentially additive, and the incremental damage imposed by one will not depend upon the level of discharge of the other.

Difficulties occur, however, if the damage function is non-linear. In this instance it will be possible to define an incremental damage function for one discharger only by holding the level of discharge of the other constant. The problem is, however, that no damage cost function can be assigned to one discharger independently of the other. Again a major problem arises in providing a given waste discharger with advance information concerning the charges to be levied on him.

The only practicable solution here may be to treat damage functions as though they were linear even when they are not precisely so. Obviously some rules of thumb will have to be worked out if the charges —or for that matter any systematic efforts to move toward an optimum —are to have practical value. Some types of damage such as corrosion appear to proceed linearly with concentration given the time of exposure. Others may well exhibit a threshold characteristic. The latter may, for example, be the case with respect to the effect of dissolved oxygen on fish life. However, even here initial appearances may deceive. Fish are usually thought to require around 4 mg/1 of dissolved oxygen to sustain life. It is true that there is virtually no negative effect until a certain loading of the receiving waters has been achieved. At least in larger bodies of water, however, there are always escape possibilities for fish, even when certain locations have less than 4 mg/1 of D.O., and actual damage to fishing consequently may proceed more or less continuously with reductions in average dissolved oxygen as escape possibilities progressively diminish. If oxygen exhaustion results, a breakpoint is again reached as aesthetic nuisance becomes significant. It may be relevant to impose charges only during certain seasons when damages actually tend to occur, and then linear functions may not be too poor an approximation of reality. Certainly here again there is a need for research on the actual character of damage functions. Empirical work of this character is almost non-existent although as already mentioned, RFF has recently launched a number of studies aimed at estimating loss functions for several important types of water uses.

II. Optimization Criteria and Charges vs.
Payments as Means to Reduce Effluent Discharge

Assume that a profit-maximizing firm has an incremental cost curve as indicated by *MC* in Figure A1.[1] Assume also that the price at which it can sell the commodity it produces is given, as indicated by the curve *D*. Initially it is also specified that the only way the firm can diminish the amount of a residual substance which it discharges into a stream is to reduce production, and that residual waste per unit of output is a constant. If a regulatory authority now imposes a unit charge on the effluent of the firm, the incremental production cost function will shift upward by the amount of the charge per unit. In the chart this is indicated by the shift of the function *MC* to *MC'*.

If on the other hand the regulatory authority offers to pay the same amount for reducing waste discharge as the unit charge previously assumed, the effect on the incremental cost function will be the same—also indicated by *MC'* in the diagram. This is true because a firm

---

[1] For an excellent exposition of the concepts and graphical devices used in this appendix, see William J. Baumol, *Economic Theory and Operations Analysis* (Englewood Cliffs, N.J.: Prentice Hall, Inc., 1962), chapter IX, "Production and Cost."

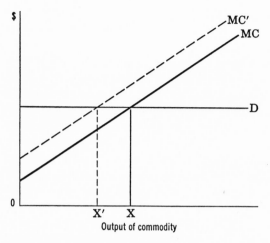

Figure A1.

rationally trying to maximize its profits will view the payment it could receive for not discharging its effluent as an opportunity cost of production since (by assumption) waste discharge is a straightforward function of production. This proposition can perhaps be clarified by the following numerical example:

Output of product	Total cost of production	Incremental cost of production	Effluent charge on waste discharge per unit of production	Payment for reduction of waste discharge per unit of production	Minimum product price necessary to induce indicated no. of units of production with charge or payment
0	10	. . .	. . .	. . .	$. . .
1	11	1	1	1	2
2	13	2	1	1	3
3	16	3	1	1	4
4	20	4	1	1	5
5	25	5	1	1	6

If, for example, the incremental cost of producing the fifth unit (neglecting the cost of waste discharge) is $5.00, and a public authority stands ready to pay $1.00 if the manufacturer does not discharge the waste associated with that unit, he will produce that unit only if the price is at least $6.00. If the price were less than $6.00, his *net* income would be higher if he simply accepted the $1.00 payment. The $1.00 payment thus becomes an *opportunity cost* even though it is not a direct outlay. The point is that in the sense of *opportunity* cost, which is the relevant concept of cost for decision purposes, the two procedures have entirely the same effect on incremental costs.

The question may well be raised whether in terms of longer-term adjustments, i.e. decisions to enter or leave a business or to expand or contract production capacity, the effect may not be different. The answer is in principle "no," but great administrative difficulties emerge if the payments route is adopted. These are discussed later.

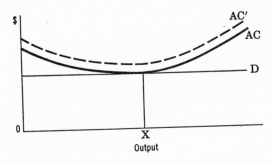

Figure A2.

In Figure A2, *AC* indicates the long-run average cost curve of a plant. This curve indicates the average costs of producing various levels of output (including an average return on investment) under conditions where the scale of plant can be adjusted to produce the given output at least over-all cost. If the price is as indicated by *D*, the firm would construct a plant for which costs were lowest at output level *X*. This is the relationship which would tend to prevail in equilibrium in a competitive industry. A charge on effluent per unit would raise the average cost function by the same amount for each unit of output. Consequently the new average cost curve would be a simple vertical displacement of the old as shown by *AC'*. A payment would have the same effect since producing an additional unit of output will always require that the firm foregoes a payment of the specified amount. Consequently the price of output must cover this payment in addition to other costs of production (including a normal return on investment) if it is to be worth while for the firm to use the resources it can command in this industry. In effect, the plant's cost curve (reflecting the value of all foregone opportunities if production is carried on) is raised by the amount of the payment if the payment is available to it whether it is producing or not.

Assume that all plants in the industry are initially earning no "excess" return (i.e., they are earning only the minimum necessary to keep their resources employed in the industry). Assume further that they have their cost curves raised by a charge or payment by the amount indicated in Figure A2. The new long-term equilibrium adjustment would then find the industry price higher by the amount of the subsidy or the payment, fewer firms in the industry, and fewer resources devoted to producing the output of the industry. All this would reflect the fact that costs imposed elsewhere in the system, and previously neglected by management, have been internalized to individual firms.

A system of charges or payments reflecting downstream costs would, however, probably not raise the opportunity costs of all firms by the same amount. Under these circumstances and assuming costs were otherwise the same, plants inducing the highest offsite costs would be selectively shut down, but the industry price would still tend to rise.

If plants are making an "excess" return (i.e. above the minimum necessary to keep them in the industry), there would not be plant shutdowns but output would be reduced and prices would tend to rise to reflect the real (opportunity) cost of production.

Since the costs associated with waste disposal are generally quite low relative to other costs of production and since the firm has the option of treating its wastes (discussed further below), their effects on prices, location, and decisions to enter or leave an industry will usually be modest. In some instances, however, this would not be the case.

Where decisions on location and/or industry entry or exit are involved, the administration of a system of subsidies becomes particularly difficult. A subsidy must be continued after shutdown of a plant, if the procedure is to have the desired results. While this might be manageable, serious problems would occur if a shift in demand for the product should increase the potential profitability of the plant, or if other dynamic adjustments should take place. Moreover, plants might introduce processes that produce a greater quantity of waste in order to obtain payment for reducing waste.

Even more perplexing would be the handling of proposals for new industrial locations. The administrative authority would have to stand ready to make payments to industries which never do locate in the area but which would do so if a payment reflecting the costs their effluents would impose were not available to them. Payments on this basis would of course be an open invitation to extortion. If charges were levied, however, the authority would only have to provide the prospective firm with an estimate of the charge to be placed on its effluent.

The possibility suggested in the text of levying charges on newly located firms and making payments to established ones would avoid some of the administrative problems associated with general use of the payments device and might appeal to many people's sense of equity.

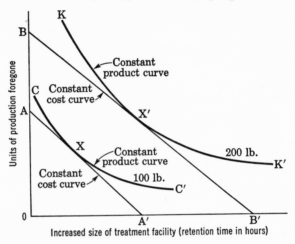

Figure A3.

Thus far, the assumption has been made that the only way in which waste loads can be reduced is by decreasing production. This was done because it lends a certain simplicity to diagrammatic exposition. It is obvious that waste loads can also be reduced by treatment. That a payment per unit reduction of waste load will produce the same balance between production cutback and treatment as a tax of equivalent amount can be conveniently shown by means of an isoquant diagram. The isoquants *CC'* and *KK'* indicate along their length a constant amount of waste reduction (say, pounds of BOD) which can be achieved by alternative combinations of treatment or production decrease.

The lines *AA'* and *BB'* indicate the number of units of treatment capacity and reduction in output that can be purchased at equal cost. Point *A'* is established by spending all of a given amount of funds on increasing treatment. Point *A* shows the number of units of production which can be foregone at the expense of an amount of net revenue equivalent to the outlay necessary to reach A' (disregarding waste disposal costs). The line AA' represents all the alternative combinations of production foregone and outlay for increased treatment which can be obtained at the same cost. The line BB' represents a similar set of alternatives for a higher cost level. For simplicity these functions are pictured as straight lines although this is not essential in order to derive the optimization criteria outlined below. An infinite number of curves like AA' and BB' corresponding to all possible levels of cost could be drawn.

Expenditure on treatment and loss of revenue on foregone production of incremental units may be in the interest of the firm either to avoid a charge on effluent or to obtain a payment for reducing discharge. A central point is that for any level of cost (outlay or foregone revenue) the firm will seek that combination of measures which will achieve the greatest waste discharge reducing effect. That combination is attained for the cost level BB' at point X' where the constant cost curve is tangent to the constant product curve KK'.

An infinite number of curves like KK' and CC' could also be drawn corresponding to each level of waste reduction. The convex to the origin slope of these curves indicates a diminishing marginal rate of substitution between the two alternatives. As treatment capacity is expanded, it substitutes less well for output reduction. Another way of saying this is that there are diminishing physical returns to increased retention time in the treatment plant.[2]

Points like X and X' indicate greatest effect at a given cost as no higher isoquant or constant product curve (in this case product refers to waste discharge reduction) is attainable given the combinations of input that can be purchased. At such points the combination of the two alternatives pictured is optimum—the rate at which one can be "traded off" for the other at the margin in order to produce a given output is equal to the ratio of their respective prices. (We can conveniently refer to the cost of output reduction and of increased treatment input as their respective prices.) The rate of tradeoff or marginal technical rate of substitution is equal to the slope of the isoquant. It is also readily demonstrable [3] that the slope of this curve equals the marginal physical product of treatment (i.e. the physical output result produced by a small increment of treatment) over the marginal physi-

---

[2] For reasons of symmetry, the assumption that waste loads decline linearly with reduction in output is retained.

[3] See Baumol, *op. cit.*, p. 184.

cal product of output reduction. Since the slope of the price line (like
AA') equals the ratio of the prices of the two alternatives we can write
the following optimizing rule:

$$\frac{MPP_T}{MPP_O} = \frac{P_T}{P_O}$$

A marginal cost function analogous to the one pictured in Figure
A1 but relating the marginal cost of an optimum combination of
waste reduction measures to the degree of waste reduction achieved
can readily be constructed from the information contained in an
isoquant diagram by establishing numerous points such as X and read-
ing off corresponding costs and outputs. The optimal waste reduction
level can then be established by equating the marginal cost of the
optimum combination of output reduction and treatment with the
charge or payment representing the downstream incremental cost.
When this condition exists the marginal costs of all relevant alternatives (including treatment, output reduction, and pollution damages)
are equated and the level of waste production and treatment is op-
timized.[4] The major point here is that since the costs of alternatives
are evaluated equivalently under the charges and payments procedures,
both the combination and level of use of alternatives will be the same.
The points previously made about administrative problems when long-
run decisions are involved are of course valid in the present context
as well.

The optimization of a combination of more than two inputs can be
conveniently shown by means of simple calculus and the method of
Lagrange multipliers.[5] (To be consistent with standard production

[4] In planning a new industrial plant the cost of an optimum combination of
treatment and effluent charges—still assuming these are the only alternatives—
would be included in the marginal cost of production, which would be compared
with marginal revenue.

[5] Let the output of waste reduction be a function of the level of use of a number of alternative inputs and let X_1 indicate the quantity of input of an alternative x_1. We can then write a production function

$$Q = f(X_1, X_2, \ldots, X_n).$$

Given any quantity of waste reduction Q^*, the firm will try to produce it as
cheaply as it can. This means it is trying to minimize its costs M (in the sense
of foregone net revenues as well as outlays) on the inputs used to produce Q^*,
where the cost is given by

$$M = P_1 X_1 + P_2 X_2 + \ldots P_n X_n,$$

where P_1 is the cost per unit of input 1, etc. The firm is constrained in minimizing M by the production function indicated above.

theory, alternative means of reducing waste loads, including output reduction, are here referred to as inputs.)

The optimizing rule developed in this appendix indicates the re-

---

This constraint can be written in the form:

$$f(X_1, X_2, \ldots, X_n) - Q^* = 0.$$

This expression is multiplied by the artificial variable λ and added to the expression M (which is to be minimized) to obtain the Lagrangian expression:

$$M_\lambda = P_1X_1 + P_2X_2 + \ldots + P_nX_n + \lambda [f(X_1, X_2, \ldots, X_n) - Q^*].$$

This expression is minimized in the standard way by setting each of its partial derivatives to zero:

$$\frac{\partial M_\lambda}{\partial X_1} = P_1 + \lambda\frac{\partial f}{\partial X_1} = 0$$

$$\frac{\partial M_\lambda}{\partial X_2} = P_2 + \lambda\frac{\partial f}{\partial X_2} = 0$$

$$\cdot \qquad \cdot \qquad \cdot \qquad \cdot$$

$$\frac{\partial M_\lambda}{\partial X_n} = P_n + \lambda\frac{\partial f}{X_n} = 0$$

$$\frac{\partial M_\lambda}{\lambda} = f(X_1, X_2, \ldots, X_n) - Q^* = 0.$$

This set of $n + 1$ simultaneous equations can be solved for the optimal values of the n inputs $X_1, X_2, \ldots, X_n$ and the Lagrangian multiplier λ.

The optimization rule indicated above can be readily derived from these equations.

If we write the first two equations as

$$P_1 = -\lambda\frac{\partial f}{\partial X_1}, \quad \text{and} \quad P_2 = -\lambda\frac{\partial f}{\partial X_2},$$

and divide one equation by the other, we get

$$\frac{P_1}{P_2} = \frac{\dfrac{\partial f}{\partial X_1}}{\dfrac{\partial f}{\partial X_2}}.$$

Since $\partial f/\partial X_1$ is equal to the marginal (physical) product of X_1 and likewise $\partial f/\partial X_2$ is the marginal product of X_2, we can write

$$\frac{P_1}{P_2} = \frac{MP_1}{MP_2},$$

which is the optimizing rule previously indicated. When this rule holds for all input combinations it also follows immediately that the cost of increasing output by a small increment by means of one input is equal to the marginal cost of increasing it by the same increment by using more of any other input. As noted several times in the text, this is the rule for minimizing costs. We have, for example, noted that in order to minimize costs associated with waste disposal in a basin the marginal cost of all relevant alternatives must be equalized.

source combination which will achieve the maximum output given the level of costs or equivalently the minimum cost for achieving a given result.

In actuality, lines like AA' and BB' would frequently be curved. They would probably be convex to the origin, since with rising marginal costs the cost per unit of reducing output would tend to rise. (There is an important distinction here between a rising price and rising incremental costs.) Straight lines (given P's) were assumed in order to simplify the derivation of the optimizing rules, and the demonstration that effluent charges and payments for waste reduction lead to the same optimizing rules. Conclusions with respect to charges and payments remain the same even if equal cost lines like AA' curve, provided certain constraints on their curvature are met.[6]

The basic and quite reasonable rule remains that in order to minimize costs the marginal costs of all relevant ways of achieving a given result must be equalized. Moreover, the result will be the same whether the cost is an actual outlay or the foregone opportunity to receive a payment.

[6] For an example of the application of isoquant analysis to a design problem where the equal cost lines curve, see Maynard M. Hufschmidt, "Application of Basic Concepts: Graphic Techniques," in Maass, *et al.*, *Design of Water Resource Systems, op. cit.*, chapter V.

5

A Study of Comparative Programs for Controlling Salinity in the Ohio

~~~~~~

Three programs are discussed in this chapter to illustrate how some of the ideas presented in the previous chapter might apply in a particular situation. The first of these is "Chloride Control Considerations for the Ohio River," a staff report prepared in 1957 for the deliberation of the Ohio River Valley Water Sanitation Commission (ORSANCO).[1] This report, subsequently cited as "Chloride Control," represents the first effort in the United States to view a waste disposal problem on a fully basin-wide basis and to articulate waste discharge at all points with a regional objective. The ORSANCO proposal, which uses a stream standards-effluent standards approach, is followed by an outline of two alternatives. The first alternative bases effluent charges on damage costs and aims at minimizing the costs associated with saline waste disposal. The second alternative is limited to the stream standards approach that underlies the ORSANCO proposal but it incorporates effluent charges.

Salinity, at least in the comparatively low concentrations foreseen in the Ohio, does not affect some of the uses which present the most difficult problems of evaluation and quantification. Nor is the problem of tracing and forecasting salinity levels complicated by the degradation processes characteristic of many other waste materials. However, by being comparatively amenable to systematic regional management,

[1] The report was made to the Commission by the ORSANCO staff and does not necessarily reflect the Commission's views.

salinity presents an opportunity to illustrate the ideas of the previous chapter in a comparatively uncomplicated form. The discussion is in terms of conditions found in humid basins such as the Ohio rather than those of arid basins where salinity often stems from natural sources and the return flow from irrigation.

Before describing and assessing the ORSANCO proposal for controlling salinity, it is useful to consider some of the more significant characteristics of salinity as a pollutant.

The relationship of salinity to other pollutants is basically additive. Within rather wide limits, salinity has little effect upon organic waste degradation processes or the virulence of toxic substances.[2] This means that the synergistic and/or cancelling effects that may occur with toxic and degradable wastes, for example, are ordinarily not present. Saline wastes can in large measure be analyzed separately from other residual materials in a water course.

Within a comparatively wide range, saline wastes have little or no effect on recreational, environmental, and health conditions. Salinity cannot be seen; within the limits ordinarily encountered it is not destructive to fish life;[3] and it is generally not dangerous to health unless concentrations become very high. A report made for the Ohio Commission by Kettering Laboratories states that there are no data to indicate that waters containing chloride up to 1,000 ppm are physiologically harmful to normal humans. Although the U.S. Public Health Service Drinking Water Standards indicate that chloride should preferably not occur in excess of 250 ppm when suitable supplies are available from other sources, drinking water supplies in the Great Plains frequently contain a multiple of the suggested concentration. The principal problem is presented by people on low sodium diets. However, they can use bottled water during seasons of high salinity, and the costs of this alternative can be evaluated.

The concentration of salinity at downstream points is relatively easy to predict if the amount discharged at upstream points is known. In contrast to waste materials subject to biochemical degradation and those that will settle out, the only process in question is dilution.

---

[2] See the discussion in Friedrich Sierp, *Gewerbliche und Industrielle Abwaesser* (Berlin: Springer-Verlag, 1959), pp. 606ff.

[3] *Ibid.*

Since salinity is not subject to treatment except at very high cost, the only economically feasible ways of reducing concentrations in watercourses are to cut back the level of salinity-discharging activities and to make fuller use of stream dilution capacity. In some instances process changes can be instituted to reduce saline discharge.

There are a number of ways in which the dilution capacity of a stream can be used more effectively: (a) wastes can be temporarily stored and discharged in a programmed manner corresponding to streamflow, (b) the streamflow pattern can be altered,[4] and (c) the salinity-discharging industries can reschedule production so as to curtail output or even temporarily shut down during the periods of low streamflow.[5]

From an economic efficiency point of view, consideration must be given to the adjustments that can be made by the industries and municipalities who use the water. These include, but are not limited to: incurring corrosion costs and temporarily shutting down salinity-sensitive plants during periods of low streamflow. The costs of these alternatives are what were referred to as damage costs in the preceding chapter.

Except for irrigated areas where the salt load is both increased and concentrated in the return flows from irrigated lands, high levels of salinity (not of natural origin) ordinarily stem from comparatively few outfalls, even in large highly developed basins. Since household water use causes only a negligible increase in salinity, municipalities make only a minor contribution to the salinity load unless their discharge includes saline industrial waste. The main source is industrial

[4] While some remarks concerning this alternative are made in a rather special context in this chapter more detailed discussion is found in chapter 2.

[5] Disposal of wastes by dilution may also be accomplished by conducting them to another basin where dilution water is more plentiful or where the effects of low quality are less severe. An extreme form of this type of disposal is conducting wastes to the sea in special waste channels. The German potash industry has evaluated a plan to conduct the wastes of the main potash-producing area to the North Sea by means of a specially constructed canal. Thus far, costs have been considered too high to permit putting such a plan into effect. Apparently waste recovery also has a rather dim current prospect as an alternative to other disposal methods. See Sierp, *op. cit.,* pp. 615–16. There is also a plan under consideration by the California Department of Water Resources to construct a waste channel in the San Joaquin Valley which would conduct waste waters, predominantly saline return flows from irrigation, to the sea. Alternatives of this scope are considered in Part III.

waste discharge, primarily from salt, potash, and crude petroleum industries. "Chloride Control" indicates that during periods of low flow at least *three-quarters* of the chloride found in the Ohio originates from industrial waste discharges, and the major part of this comes from one tributary—the Muskingum.

QUALITY CRITERIA AND THE STREAM STANDARDS

The quality criteria upon which the "Chloride Control" recommendations for a control program are based are as follows:

Chloride-ion concentration

Public supplies:
Acceptable	Less than 125 ppm
Doubtful	125-250 ppm
Unsatisfactory	More than 250 ppm

Industrial supplies:
Acceptable	Less than 50 ppm
Doubtful	50-175 ppm
Unsatisfactory	More than 175 ppm

Salinity is not considered to have any significant effect on water uses other than for public supplies and industrial purposes.

When the report matched findings with respect to chloride in the Ohio River against its quality criteria, it was revealed that in one stretch of the river "unsatisfactory" concentrations are being approached. Periods of quality impairment violating the criteria may therefore be expected as a result of industrial expansion. The report suggests, however, that by timely institution of a control program based on "proportionate discharge," the river can accommodate chloride-bearing wastes and still meet acceptable quality conditions.

"Chloride Control" proposes that the Commission "adopt a control program which would limit chloride concentrations in the Ohio River at points of use for public and industrial supplies from exceeding (1) a monthly average concentration of 125 ppm at all flows above and including the minimum monthly average flow (called the design flow) that has a probability of occurrence once in ten years; and (2) a maximum concentration of 250 ppm at any time."

The monthly average limiting value of 125 ppm is recommended because ". . . water of this quality is within the acceptable range for public supplies and would not be unsatisfactory for cooling purposes, which is the major industrial use." (p. 6.)

With respect to the design flow, "Chloride Control" states "Once-in-10-year drought severity or minimum flow provides a reasonable factor of safety in the design of a chloride control program for the maintenance of satisfactory quality of water for public supplies and for major industrial uses. If, in the opinion of the Commission a greater degree of protection is desired, the 15 or 20 year minimum flow could be substituted; if a lesser degree of assurance is considered adequate, then the 5-year flow might be chosen." (p. 34.)

More will be said about the quality criteria and the design flow when the problem of evaluating damages is addressed later. At this point it may be noted, however, that only the most fragmentary evidence was available concerning the costs of salinity to industrial water users. The evidence that could be marshalled related to isolated instances of damages experienced as a result of a given time of exposure to a given concentration. It provided little basis for determining a functional relationship between different levels of salinity and damage costs to water users. Without better information from industry, it will be difficult to avoid rather arbitrary, ill-informed, and inefficient regulation procedures.

THE ORSANCO STAFF PROPOSAL

The general idea of the control program suggested by the ORSANCO staff is that waste discharges upstream are to be cut back in a pre-arranged, proportional manner during periods of low flow in order to avoid violating the stated quality conditions at some downstream point of use. The point of use selected was Huntington, West Virginia, which is the point on the main stem presently experiencing the highest concentration.

The report states that at present the quality standards are not violated. During low-flow periods the existing chloride load in the river at Huntington is just about in balance with the assimilative capacity.

Further expansion of industry on the river would require reduction of discharge during critical periods if the specified standards are to be met. While it is not explicitly stated, presumably the primary means of accomplishing this would be temporary storage of some of the wastes during periods of low flow.[6] Temporary storage and programmed discharge is already used to some extent by the pulp and paper industry,[7] and by the chemical industry.[8]

Two programs for cutting back saline discharges during periods of low flow were recommended as possibilities, but only Proposal A, the one preferred by the ORSANCO staff is presented here. The following outline of Proposal A and the staff's view of its merits are quoted directly from "Chloride Control," pp. 36, 37, and 38. The subheads were inserted as an aid to comparing this proposal with an alternative based on damage costs and effluent charges.

Chloride from Industries

"This proposal outlines a system for instituting: (a) a uniform-percentage cutback of both main-stem and tributary loads when desired quality conditions at a main-stem point of use would be exceeded; coupled with (b) final adjustment of tributary cutbacks contingent upon the relative amount of dilution water furnished by the tributary.

"This system introduces a principle in water-pollution control prac-

---

[6] It is interesting to note in this regard that discharge programmed in correspondence with streamflow is quite common in the German potash-producing regions. Among the streams primarily affected are the Werra, the Weser, and the Aller. In the area of the Werra River, for example, the responsible authorities have made it mandatory that (potash) waste discharges be co-ordinated with streamflow and that the discharger install equipment which automatically measures and records the amount and specific gravity of the effluent. Releases are scheduled according to a release table which indicates both the stream stage and the content of chlorides in the stream. The control houses are outfitted with instruments which indicate the quality of the stream, the quality of the effluent, and the stream stage. Sierp, *op. cit.*, p. 613.

[7] See Daniel A. Okun, James C. Lamb, III, and C. C. Wells, Jr., *A Waste Control Program for a River with Highly Variable Flow*, presented at the 17th Purdue Industrial Waste Conference, May 1-3, 1962.

[8] See *Index of TVA News*, Technical Library, Knoxville, Tennessee, September 13, 1962, item 140803.

tice that might be termed the Golden Rule concept for sharing assimilative capacity with others as you would have them share with you. Application of the principle calls for the recognition of two conditions: (1) that the dilution water (flow) contributed by a tributary offers a fair means for a rational determination of relative equity allocation; and (2) the flows from tributaries during low flow approximate the same ratio as do the areas of the drainage basins.

"Under this system of control, proportionate discharge would be practiced in accordance with the following procedures:

Basis for Controlling Discharge

"1. Quality conditions desired at a main stem point-of-use would serve as the basis for regulating upstream discharges of chloride waste. This means that the interstate point-of-use where the highest concentration of chloride occurs would be the control point.

Adjusting Discharge to Flow

"2. Quality control at a point of use would be achieved by scheduling the discharge of chloride wastes above that point. This means that the amount discharged from a source must be proportioned to the availability of streamflow. Variation in flow, therefore, is the determining factor in establishing schedules of permitted discharge.

Control of Tributary Loads

"3. Chloride affecting a point of use on the Ohio River emanates from wastes discharged into: (a) tributaries; and (b) directly into the main stem. Because Commission concern with intrastate streams is limited to the quality of the tributary only as it enters the main stem, each tributary load would be recognized as a single source of chloride. Thus, the total chloride load at a point of use on the main stem is the sum of the tributary loads and the individual discharges to the main stem from industries and municipalities.

Dilution Water

"4. Dilution water available at the control point on the Ohio River would be considered as the sum total of the flow contributed from each of the upstream tributary drainage basins.

Chloride Quotas for Drainage Basins

"5. Because chloride capacity of a stream is a direct function of flow, it is possible under any given set of circumstances to establish for each drainage basin a chloride allotment based on the load conditions existing at the control point. Establishment of a chloride allotment in proportion to contributed flow, and related to the loads on the main stem and the tributaries, is an equitable method for the allocation of total available capacity. It recognizes that each drainage basin in the Compact district should be entitled to that share of chloride capacity as determined by load conditions at an interstate point-of-use and for which it can provide the proportionate amount of dilution water.

Adjusting Quotas

"6. The quota for any drainage basin, it should be noted, represents a proportionate share of capacity; it is not a quantity fixed for all time. As new or expanded industries in the district seek accommodation for their waste loads (either on a tributary or on the main stem of the Ohio River) the allotment previously assigned to various drainage basins would be uniformly adjusted, along with the permitted discharge from main-stem sources of chloride. How often such revisions might be required is wholly dependent on the location and size of new loads. Presumably, adjustments would be made only at periodic intervals.

Basins Contributing Heavy Salinity Loads

"7. Application of the uniform percentage-reduction rule to chloride discharges from upstream drainage basins would be made with regard to establishing a balance between contributed load and allotment. At present there is at least one tributary drainage basin in the district that contributes a chloride load far in excess of its proportionate allotment as determined by dilution water. There are other drainage basins whose contribution of chloride is less than their calculated allotments based on the dilution water they supply. The interests of equity would not be served, therefore, without first imposing cutbacks on all those basins that exceed their allotments and until all of the drainage basins are in approximate balance.

Information Provided to and by Industry

"8. Once the proportionate allotment for a drainage basin has been established, a load-discharge schedule based on flow variations would be computed for main-stem industries and for each tributary. These schedules would be prepared by the Commission staff in consultation with the state agencies and then submitted to the Commission for consideration; after adoption by the Commission the schedules would be referred to the states for appropriate action with their industries. Discharge schedules for individual industries would be referenced to flow as recorded at a stream-gauging station from which the industrial plant can obtain readings. Effective conduct of the program necessitates some form of record on discharges be maintained by each industrial plant for transmittal to the state agency with copies to the Commission.

Chloride from Municipalities

"Control of chloride from municipalities presents a special problem. The chloride content of sewage cannot be lagooned or otherwise handled on a proportionate-discharge basis such as industrial wastes. Yet some form of control should be exercised because municipal sewage could be abnormally loaded with chloride as the result of certain types of industrial activity within the community.

"It is recommended, therefore, that after a control program has been inaugurated the Commission authorize an investigation of chloride content from municipal sewage-treatment works. Where it is determined that the sewage contains abnormal concentrations of chloride, then the municipality should be placed under compulsion by the state agency to which it is responsible for determining the origin of the chloride within its system and institute necessary controls.

Merits of Proposal A

"Here are the salient reasons why Proposal A recommends itself for consideration:

"From the viewpoint of rationality, the proposal rests on the sound practice of relating control to quality conditions as revealed at a point of use. Further, the control is exercised in accordance with the ability of a stream to assimilate the wastes.

"In addition, a method is provided for an equitable allocation of stream capacity among the states and their industries.

"The permitted discharge of waste is regulated in accordance with a flow variation—as, when and where that flow occurs.

"It places responsibility directly on the producer of the waste for regulating his discharge in accordance with a regional pattern of control.

"Within limitations imposed by conditions in the main stem, control of industrial loads discharged to tributaries is solely within jurisdiction of the states involved."

PROPOSAL BASED ON DAMAGE COSTS AND EFFLUENT CHARGES

In the following pages it is suggested that a system of charges for effluent discharge based on damage costs might have a number of advantages over the proposal in "Chloride Control." Such a procedure would tend toward a minimization of costs for any given waste load and would tend to lead to an optimum amount of waste discharge. To indicate the general character of the "charges" alternative and to provide some preliminary assessment of it, the points outlined above with respect to the proportional cutback proposal are restated in terms of the principles and criteria of a system of charges. Elaborations of a number of the points made are found in chapter 4 and its appendices. Discussion of information requirements and administrative costs is postponed until later.

Chloride from Industries

Basis for Controlling Discharge

1. The cost of downstream damages would serve as the basis for effluent charges and would provide the incentive for regulating up-

stream discharges of chloride waste. This means that there would be no single control point downstream. Control at any outfall would be a straightforward function of downstream damages.

Adjusting Discharge to Flow

2. Quality control at points of use would be achieved by causing upstream polluters to view an estimate of incremental downstream damages, as an opportunity cost in making their own production, plant design, and location decisions.[9]

Unless there is a fully compensating variation in discharge the level of salinity will rise during low-flow periods, and consequently downstream damages and effluent charges will also increase. The increased charges provide an incentive for industry to institute temporary lagooning combined with programmed discharge of wastes, output adjustments, and perhaps other measures. The waste discharger will have an incentive to engage in each of these alternatives until their individual incremental costs equal the user charges (downstream damages) which they avoid. An individual polluter will find it worthwhile to discharge in an unchanged fashion only if the charges levied upon him for downstream damages are less than the cost of avoiding them.

Control of Tributary Loads

3. Chloride affecting points of use on the Ohio River emanates from waste discharged into (a) tributaries, and (b) directly into the main stem. Because Commission concern with intrastate streams is limited to the quality of the tributary only as it enters the main stem, each tributary load would be recognized as a single source of chloride. Thus, the total chloride load at points of use on the main stem is the sum of the tributary loads and the individual discharges to the main stem from industries and municipalities higher up in the

---

[9] Damages imposed by the effluent from a particular outfall at a given level of discharge and streamflow would be added together. Since downstream damages occur in a series of uses, the principle is to equate the sum of the marginal damages to the marginal cost of upstream abatement measures. For a discussion of the principles involved in this "adding together" approach, see George S. Tolley and V. S. Hastings, "Optimal Water Allocations, The North Platte River," *Quarterly Journal of Economics*, May, 1960.

drainage basin. Charges will be applied to tributaries and main-stem polluters in an identical fashion, i.e., each tributary will be taken as an individual outfall. The amount of each outfall's contribution to salinity at various downstream points will be computed and the resulting damages evaluated. In assessing downstream costs, the dilution contributed by a tributary is essentially irrelevant.[10] For example, in the situation illustrated in Figure 6, all the plants could move to a single tributary or the main stem above the point of confluence without altering downstream main stem costs. On the other hand, such moves would alter the costs occurring on the tributaries themselves or on the upper main stem.

This procedure suggests how pricing can serve to co-ordinate the activities of an authority on a main stem which has large amounts of dilution capacity and scattered sources of pollution with the activities of an authority on an intensely developed tributary like the Muskingum or the Mahoning. (These activities might include system design, construction, and operation.) The authority on the main stem would view the residual amount of waste delivered by a tributary as a waste outfall, and it would levy upon the tributary authority the costs which these wastes impose downstream. Costs on the main stem would vary with the over-all amount of dilution available. However, costs at points of use on the main stem would in no way depend upon the origin of the dilution water. The tributary authority on which downstream costs are assessed would then be induced to view them as opportunity costs in its own quality management activities and design and operate its system accordingly.

If the tributary authority augments flow during low-flow periods, an amendment of the above line of reasoning is in order. To *provide an appropriate incentive* to the tributary authority to use this device, it should be credited with the incremental reduction in main stem costs which results from enhanced dilution on the main stem. Further discussion of flow augmentation and other measures to alter the assimilative capacity of streams is presented in Part III.

If the tributary authority did not build and operate facilities for salinity control, but did adhere to the principles indicated in this

[10] An exception occurs when low-flow augmentation on a tributary results in increased dilution on the main stem.

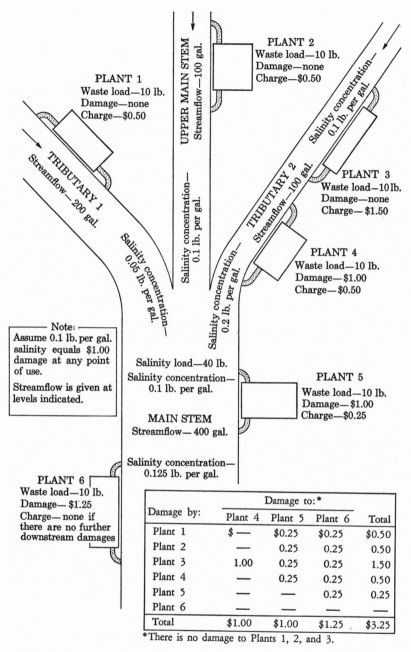

PLANT 1
Waste load—10 lb.
Damage—none
Charge—$0.50

PLANT 2
Waste load—10 lb.
Damage—none
Charge—$0.50

UPPER MAIN STEM
Streamflow—100 gal.

TRIBUTARY 1
Streamflow—200 gal.

Salinity concentration—
0.05 lb. per gal.

Salinity concentration—
0.1 lb. per gal.

Salinity concentration—
0.1 lb. per gal.

PLANT 3
Waste load—10 lb.
Damage—none
Charge—$1.50

TRIBUTARY 2
Streamflow—100 gal.

Salinity concentration—
0.2 lb. per gal.

PLANT 4
Waste load—10 lb.
Damage—$1.00
Charge—$0.50

Note:
Assume 0.1 lb. per gal.
salinity equals $1.00
damage at any point
of use.

Streamflow is given at
levels indicated.

Salinity load—40 lb.
Salinity concentration—
0.1 lb. per gal.

MAIN STEM
Streamflow—400 gal.

PLANT 5
Waste load—10 lb.
Damage—$1.00
Charge—$0.25

Salinity concentration—
0.125 lb. per gal.

PLANT 6
Waste load—10 lb.
Damage—$1.25
Charge—none if
there are no further
downstream damages

| Damage by: | Damage to:* | | | |
	Plant 4	Plant 5	Plant 6	Total
Plant 1	$ —	$0.25	$0.25	$0.50
Plant 2	—	0.25	0.25	0.50
Plant 3	1.00	0.25	0.25	1.50
Plant 4	—	0.25	0.25	0.50
Plant 5	—	—	0.25	0.25
Plant 6	—	—	—	—
Total	$1.00	$1.00	$1.25	$3.25

*There is no damage to Plants 1, 2, and 3.

Figure 6. Schematic illustration of salinity discharges and damages on the tributaries and main stem of a river system.

study, it would assess the costs arising within the tributary and an appropriate portion of main-stem user charges to the individual dischargers. The latter would be based upon the individual discharger's contribution to the salinity load discharging into the main stem.

The proposed system of tributary charges could be carried as far through a river complex as merited by the existence of technological external diseconomies.

Dilution Water

4. No separate attention would need to be given to, or allowance made for, dilution capacity contributed by the individual upstream tributary drainage basins, except for low-flow augmentation as noted above.

Chloride Quotas for Drainage Basins

5. See 4.

Adjusting Quotas

6. See 4.

Basins Contributing Heavy Salinity Loads

7. Application of charges to wastes discharged from tributaries would result in a heavy charge upon tributaries like the Muskingum which contribute absolutely large waste loads. Other things equal, this would result in large absolute reductions of waste loads from these tributaries. However, all other dischargers would have an incentive, proportionate to downstream costs imposed, to cut back on waste discharge.

Information Provided to and by Industry

8. Once a schedule of charges has been established for each level of flow and each major outfall, the individual plants are left to make their own flow discharge schedules. Charges to the individual industrial plant or tributary will be based on the flow recorded at a stream-gauging station from which the industrial plant or authority responsible for the tributary can obtain readings. For planning purposes each

plant should be provided with an estimate of the "expected value" [11] of damages per unit of its waste discharge.

Each plant should maintain a record of its discharges, preferably by an automatic recording device, for transmittal to the state agency with copies to the Commission. Since the appropriate basis for the charge is chloride load rather than effluent volume, the salinity of the discharged water should also be recorded. The system of charges will not have a "design flow" but will view damages and user charges as continuously variable. At streamflows above certain levels, damages will probably be so small that it will not pay to administer the system. It may be found, for example, that flow conditions on the Ohio during the next decade or so are not low enough each season or even year to merit putting the program into operation.

Chloride from Municipalities

Control of chloride from municipalities presents a special problem since it is ordinarily not feasible to segregate chlorides from the municipal sewage or to treat them, and, in the case of large cities, temporary lagooning of total waste effluent is usually very costly.

It is recommended, however, that chloride stemming from municipal outfalls be assessed on the same basis as that from industrial outfalls. This would prompt municipalities to determine the origin of the chloride concentrations and to assess charges on the originators, who would then have an incentive for reducing discharges.

Merits of the Charges Alternative

The proposal rests on the principle of economic efficiency that output, process design and management, and waste disposal decisions should be made in light of all opportunity costs. The proposed system of charges would impose a social opportunity cost, which an enterprise escapes when discharge is not regulated. By the same token, the system charges would induce upstream abatement activity only to the extent that incremental downstream damage costs exceed incre-

[11] The concept of "expected value" is explained on p. 131.

mental upstream abatement costs. The quality of water in the stream would be a *dependent variable* rather than a *prescribed standard.*

This procedure would tend to induce optimum use of the stream's capacity to dilute wastes, as it would tend to minimize the costs associated with a given level of waste to be disposed of and provide an incentive to produce an optimum amount of waste.

The objective of the cost distribution is to optimize resources allocation. If the resulting income distribution is not considered equitable, subsidies should be paid directly, but in a manner that does not induce inefficient behavior on the part of the recipient.

The varying of charges with streamflow provides an incentive for regulating discharge in correspondence with streamflow. However, such regulation of discharge is not mandatory. If a waste discharger finds it expensive to provide temporary storage of wastes, he may simply pay the charge. On the other hand, in instances where effluent storage can be provided inexpensively, or where product output can be economically stored and diverted to other time periods, the charges will be avoided to varying extents.

The suggested procedure places responsibility directly on the producer of the waste for taking action which is efficient from the social as well as the private point of view. It does not impose any arbitrarily determined course of action on him.

The appropriate handling of industrial waste loads discharged into tributaries is a function of the authorities responsible for the tributaries upon which the charge is levied. Whatever action the authorities take will have to be taken in light of downstream cost.

INFORMATION REQUIREMENTS
OF THE TWO APPROACHES

The two approaches outlined are not fully symmetrical as to objective or effect, and this influences the amount of information they require. The objective of the system of charges is to approximate an economically optimum level of salinity at lowest costs; it takes into consideration both the damage costs imposed on the water users and the abatement costs incurred by the waste dischargers. Other things being equal, the discharger whose wastes enter far upstream and consequently are reused a large number of times will bear a higher charge and therefore have a greater incentive to introduce more far-reaching control measures than a waste discharger farther downstream. For each waste discharger, the incremental abatement costs will tend to be equated with the charges (damage costs). Framing such a system of charges requires reasonable approximations of the incremental downstream costs imposed by individual effluent discharges.

In preparing "Chloride Control," the ORSANCO staff made some evaluation of salinity damages as a basis for setting the salinity tolerance limits.

The staff disregarded damages to the environment, to recreation, to degradation of organic wastes, and to public health since these hardly come into question over the range of salinity concentrations which can currently be foreseen in the Ohio. Similarly, effects on navigation equipment were disregarded because there ". . . is no information available to the Commission staff that would suggest a quantitative relationship of chloride in fresh water streams and corrosion of boathulls, dams, locks, bridges, and dock structures." [12] For the same reason, no criterion was suggested with respect to hydro-electric power.

The only damages to Ohio River water uses which require evaluation in order to institute a system of charges, consequently, are some aspects of public water supply and industrial water uses.

Two aspects of public water supply come into question—palatability and corrosiveness. Within the range of salinity expected in the Ohio, palatability would be affected very little, if at all, and corrosive effects would likely be limited to hot water systems.[13] With regard to evaluation of the cost of corrosion, one study has reported the "final determination of the corrosion effects of a new increment of supply or a change in treatment must usually be determined for each specific case by means of a series of empirical tests. As a result of these tests and a knowledge of the techniques and costs of corrosion inhibition, esti-

[12] "Chloride Control," p. 18.
[13] Palatability presents difficulties in evaluation which corrosion and other physical destruction do not. Some evidence of its economic value might, however, be found by investigating bottled water sales for areas with differing levels of salinity in their public supplies.

mates can be made of the cost of corrosion and the cost of possible inhibition treatments." [14]

Studies of this kind could yield cost functions in terms of salinity level and period of exposure, and the cost of the studies should not be a major obstacle to implementing a program of charges.

Without doubt the most important damaging effect of advancing salinity levels on the Ohio will be to industrial users. "Chloride Control" indicates that three general classifications of industrial water use claim consideration. These are cooling water, processing water, and boiler feed water, with cooling water being quantitatively by far the most important use (93 per cent of total intake).

Not only is information concerning industrial damages deficient for introducing a system of charges, but the cutback suggested in "Chloride Control" does not seem to be related to any systematic study of costs and gains, probably in large measure because information was difficult to obtain from industry. The estimates of industrial damage in *cooling* water applications reported in "Chloride Control" are a handful of examples from steel mills in which salinity concentrations are stated as threshold values. A representative of a steel corporation is quoted in the report as saying that concentrations of salinity above 175 ppm chloride content would cause pitting of rollers. The Bethlehem Steel Corporation agreement with the City of Baltimore is quoted as stipulating that the chloride content shall not exceed 175 ppm calculated on the basis of monthly averages. A consulting engineer is quoted as saying that water with more than 50 ppm of chlorides would be unsatisfactory for the production of stainless steel. The evidence cited on corrosion of condenser tubes related only to very extreme values. There was no indication that *costs* had been determined and related in any systematic way to a range of chloride concentrations.

Research to identify the costs to industrial users associated with various levels of water quality is urgently needed and is in part under way. Clearly, such research can only be successful if industry cooperates. The alternative to rational control schemes based on ade-

[14] Jack Hirshleifer, James DeHaven, and Jerome Milliman, *Water Supply: Economics, Technology, and Policy* (Chicago: University of Chicago Press, 1960), p. 198.

quate information is rule-of-thumb control schemes which will often prove arbitrary and costly.

"Chloride Control" quotes a statement by Harold A. Thomas, Jr., Professor of Civil and Sanitary Engineering at Harvard, in which he says in part, "There is some evidence for believing the threshold concentration for corrosion damage is lower than the 50 ppm figure sometimes quoted. This is based in part upon the fact that chloride increases corrosion by increasing the conductivity, and conductivity increases about in direct proportion to chloride increases." (p. 15.)

This suggests that the notion of a threshold value which is embodied in the proportional cutback approach may not be entirely appropriate. The charges approach does not imply a threshold value, but views costs as being a continuous function of chloride concentrations. Moreover, Professor Thomas' statement suggests that damage may be approximately a linear function of concentration and duration.[15] If this is the case, the determination and assessment of costs will be much less complex than if these relationships were not linear (see chapter 4).

Information provided by the Interstate Commission on the Delaware to the ORSANCO staff indicates that in a number of process-water applications the losses may also be approximated by a linear function. However, this presumption must also be subjected to systematic empirical investigation.

All of the major damages which salinity may cause in the Ohio appear to be amenable to reasonable quantification. Moreover, there is some presumption that damages will in some circumstances turn out to be a comparatively simple function of levels of salinity and duration of these levels.

A PROGRAM TO APPROXIMATE
A MORE LIMITED OBJECTIVE

A system of effluent charges could also be used to achieve the objective indicated in ORSANCO Proposal A of meeting specified

---

[15] This assumption also underlies the study by Rolf Eliassen and Walter F. Rowland, *Industrial Benefits Derived from Improved Raw Water Quality in the Contra Costa Canal,* Publication No. 3, Project on Engineering-Economic Planning, Stanford University, 1962.

levels of salinity at a selected downstream control plant. The procedure in this case would be to set a uniform charge per unit of salinity discharged. This would have certain advantages over the ORSANCO required proportionate cutback upstream. First, the level at which the user charge must be set to be effective would provide an estimate of the marginal cost of meeting the standard, which is a vital piece of information for evaluating the policy. Second, the standard would tend to be met at lower real resources cost. Cutbacks, either by means of lagooning or production adjustments, would tend to be made where it is most economical to do so rather than in an arbitrary across-the-board fashion. To achieve the required degree of withholding at minimum cost, the incremental costs of withholding must be equalized. This will tend to occur if all discharges have a uniform effluent charge levied upon them. It would not occur if all dischargers were required to cut back proportionally. Those dischargers who find it less expensive to pay the charges than to control discharge would of course do so. The funds paid to the control authority do not represent a use of resources and are available for other purposes. Possible uses of these funds were discussed in the previous chapter.

To achieve even the circumscribed objective of meeting certain set standards at a control point by the use of charges, the control authority would need more information than if it simply ordered a proportionate cutback of all discharges. If the cutback were arbitrary, no information would be needed at all. However, a responsible authority will probably make at least a rough calculation of the cost of withholding discharge under representative conditions before ordering a proportionate cutback. This information could be made to yield an estimate of the response to various levels of charges which could serve as a basis for an initial system of charges. Since some investment is usually needed to respond efficiently to effluent charges, the authority should make known its initial schedule of charges and indicate the charges per unit of salinity for each level of streamflow, or more directly the "expected value" of the probability distribution of charges. The schedule of charges could then be adjusted to accord with the degree to which the initial schedule missed its goal and to reflect changing conditions such as the location of new industries. In short, the central merit of the charges approach is that it would tend toward an equalization of incremental costs of abatement at each discharge point. This means that the standard would be achieved with least possible value of resources use.

Part III

Regional Waste Disposal Systems

~~~~~~

Until now it has been assumed that there are no efficient quality control measures that cannot be realized at the individual waste outfall or water supply intake. The assumption that such facilities could not reduce the costs associated with waste disposal in a basin was useful for discussion of the maldistribution of costs resulting from "technological external diseconomies," and probably descriptive of an important number of real cases as well. However, there are instances where economies can be realized by collective waste treatment, low-flow augmentation, stream reaeration, and measures such as the specialized use of streams or stretches of streams. Where facilities involve scale economies which cannot be efficiently realized at individual outfalls or intakes or where the use of particular facilities is inhibited for other reasons, it may be desirable to have a regional authority with powers more extensive than those assumed in earlier chapters. These may extend to design and possibly construction and operation of facilities.

The river basin or sub-basin authority which would design, construct, operate, and finance virtually all abatement measures and the authority which simply sees to it that (through effluent charges or standards) downstream costs are more or less well reflected in the upstream decisions of managerially independent units are extreme cases.

The provision of a wide range of collective facilities will tend to be of particular advantage in heavily populated industrial areas. It must be understood, however, that in some, perhaps many, basins in this country there may be little or no opportunity to benefit from collective abatement measures other than augmentation of flow through releases from reservoir storage. In these cases the economic problem is to assure that treatment, process and product adjustments, and damages at individual points of outfall and intake approximate an optimal relationship to one another and to the enhancement of low flows.

One can, of course, think of any number of possible combinations of planning, construction, and operation of quality control measures, incentives to individual decision units to behave optimally, and/or administrative regulation in a basin. No attempt will be made to be exhaustive with respect to these possibilities.

One point should be noted here. In general terms, the economic design and operation criteria are identical in each situation when the objective is the optimal management of the water quality of the basin. The major problem is to articulate the decisions which are left to fiscally independent units in an optimal way with those made directly by the regional authority. An authority concerned with water resources does not possess the scope, even in principle, to decide all courses of action bearing upon the way water resources are used. For example, if such an authority decided that firm A should be located at site 1 because its wastes could be handled cheaply there, it might force firm A to incur transportation or other costs greater than the saving in waste disposal costs. Due to such possibilities and even probabilities, decisions on location, production, and the character of production processes should *never* be based exclusively on considerations of water cost and waste disposal. Nevertheless, it is important to develop means whereby these considerations can be brought to bear on the decisions of firms and of public agencies with competence in other aspects of land use planning. It is suggested that systems of charges have special merit for this purpose.

6

Regional Water Quality Management Systems Including Large-Scale Measures

~~~~~~

This chapter focuses first on the problems involved in planning or designing an optimum regional waste disposal system. In other words, the question of the *scale* of various measures and facilities is addressed. In addition, some economic problems of optimal operation of existing systems are analyzed.

Ideally a basin agency operating in a basin where substantial scale economies in water quality management exist should plan and implement a system which equates the relevant[1] incremental costs associated with waste disposal in all directions. These costs include all manner of waste treatment and water supply treatment, methods of flow regulation (including opportunity costs which arise out of the value of storage for alternative uses), methods of conforming waste discharge to streamflow, changes in industrial processes and output, changes in industrial location, *and waste discharge damages.* More information is required to achieve an optimum system in the situation where actual system design by a regional authority is desirable than

---

[1] The term "relevant" is quite important here. It does not mean that the marginal costs of treatment, for example, will be equal everywhere. Indeed, as explained in earlier chapters the costs of treatment or other abatement measures will be higher at upstream points than at downstream ones in an optimal system. What it does mean is that optimality demands that it be impossible to make marginal "tradeoffs" and thereby reduce costs. The reason why there can be higher marginal costs upstream is that the hydrology of the stream does not permit downstream waste reduction activities to be reflected in upstream water quality. This point is expanded later.

when appropriate allocation of costs induces an approximately optimum system.

Under U.S. conditions, low-flow augmentation of streams by means of releases from reservoir storage would often be an element in an optimum system. Relationships of complementarity and substitution exist between flow augmentation and other aspects of multipurpose development such as navigation, irrigation, flood control, and hydroelectric power generation, and these relationships must be considered in computing the opportunity costs of utilizing flow augmentation for water quality improvement. Thus the planning of efficient systems for waste disposal and water supply is ordinarily an integral element of the over-all water resources planning problem.

In sum, ideally the results of all relevant water resources system designs and operating procedures would have to be considered and a solution derived which simultaneously indicated the optimum combination of system elements and their operating procedures. In industrial areas the solution would entail a system of charges and/or other measures such as effluent standards and zoning in order to secure the optimum amounts and locations of waste discharge. If this were successfully done, the solution would be "efficient," maximum net benefit would be obtained from the available water resources, and, as the latter implies, the over-all cost associated with the disposal of an optimum amount of wastes would be minimized.

The problem of designing optimal waste disposal systems in conjunction with over-all basin planning becomes more complex when hydrologic variability is considered, since the concentration of most pollutants in stream waters is inversely related to the rate of flow. This gives rise to a problem concerning the critical flow against which protection is to be sought.[2] Moreover, hydrology is a fundamental factor in the proper assessment of effluent charges since it affects both the costs of operating the regional disposal system and the residual damages resulting from waste disposal.

---

[2] For a fuller discussion of the problem of the "design flow" see Allen V. Kneese, *Water Pollution* (Washington: Resources for the Future, Inc., 1962), chapter IV. Much work on the system design problems presented by hydrological uncertainty has been done by the Harvard Water Resources group. See Arthur Maass, *et al.*, *Design of Water Resource Systems* (Cambridge: Harvard University Press, 1962), especially chapters 3, 9, 10 and 11.

In principle, the reduction of wastes and of waste concentrations should be carried out until the costs of all relevant means of abatement and the "mathematical expectation" of damages avoided are equalized at the margin. (The concept of mathematical expectation or "expected value" is explained later in this chapter.) The principle just stated could be applied rather straightforwardly if the probable costs imposed by pollution (equipment damage, increased treatment cost, recreational opportunities foregone, environmental deterioration, etc.) could be integrated into a single monetary measure of value. Under these circumstances, design flow should be treated as a dependent variable, which is determined by the outcome of the economic analysis. This principle is also explained below. Some of the effects of water quality deterioration, however, are not, or not yet, measurable by market prices or imputed values based upon willingness to pay. This difficulty, as previously indicated, arises from the presence of collective goods aspects,[3] interdependencies in consumption, and other problems. The possibility of assessing these values has been discussed in Part II.

Means must be found for reflecting the value of recreational opportunities, environmental benefits of stream sanitation, social public health values, and perhaps others in efficiently designed systems, even though the ability to measure individual willingness to pay for them is limited at the present time.

THE BASIN-WIDE FIRM AGAIN

The example of a basin-wide firm is used here, as it was earlier, as a means of clarifying economic principles. It is not suggested as an

[3] At first sight, flow augmentation to avoid damage from waste disposal would appear to be a "public" or "collective" good since access to it cannot readily be controlled and there is little or no incentive for a waste discharger to provide it for himself. However, it is not a collective good in the sense generally accepted by economists. Paul Samuelson has identified such goods as ones "which all enjoy in common in the sense that each individual's consumption of such a good leads to no subtraction from any other individual's consumption of that good. . . ." "The Pure Theory of Public Expenditure," *The Review of Economics and Statistics*, November, 1954, p. 387. One waste discharger's use of dilution capacity obviously eliminates the use of the same unit by others. Formally this means that individual demands for the dilution of effluents (based on the cost of alternative measures)

answer, for it has its own disadvantages. It cannot take account of uses that are not reflected by market values, and, as a monopoly, it would present problems of regulation.

The point of the example is to illustrate some of the principles involved in taking account of the technical interdependencies along a stream when economies of large scale in quality management measures are available. Assume that a single firm conducts all water-using industrial enterprises, all water and sewerage utilities (no privately owned septic tanks, water softeners, etc.), and all water transportation and related facilities. Assume further that the firm operates all hydroelectric facilities, owns all land and structures in the flood plain, and is the sole provider of flow regulation. Finally, assume that the firm operates in markets that are either competitive or in which public regulatory authorities set prices equal to marginal costs at levels of output which just clear the market.

The decision criteria which the firm would use in regard to disposal of wastes in order to *maximize its profits* (or, if appropriate, minimize its losses) are those generally appropriate to other aspects of optimum resource use confronted by the firm. The firm would select the combination of water quality control measures (water supply treatment, sewage treatment, flow augmentation, co-ordinated releases, etc.) and downstream damages that would minimize the over-all costs associated with disposal of its wastes at its most profitable level of activity. This would be accomplished by equating the relevant incremental costs associated with waste disposal for all alternatives.

As an example of the principle of equal relevant incremental cost, assume that the only alternatives are sewage treatment and pollution damages (corrosion, hardness, reduced cooling efficiency, etc.). The firm would then operate so as to equate marginal treatment costs with marginal residual damages. If it did not, there would still be an opportunity to reduce over-all costs by shifting between the alternatives.

The firm would transport effluent to a collective treatment plant where scale economies can be realized, if this is less costly than treatment at the discharge point. In fact, the firm would continue to trans-

---

must be added horizontally rather than vertically. Flow augmentation is perhaps best considered an extreme form of scale economy in abatement measures.

port effluent to lower cost plants until the marginal costs of transportation and the marginal treatment cost saved are equal.

Since transporting wastes long distances and building scattered treatment plants are usually expensive procedures, the firm would weigh these diseconomies of scattered development in the balance with other such diseconomies (water supply) and perhaps certain economies (less congestion), and the optimum compactness of development would be produced.

Compact development might be influenced by certain physical characteristics of the stream. Since the rate of reaeration through the air-water interface is directly proportional to the oxygen deficit, the organic waste degradation capacity of a stream increases as the load placed upon it increases. This, plus the possibility of stream treatment to take advantage of economies of scale, emphasizes the possibilities of stream specialization as a means of reducing the costs associated with waste disposal. Again the firm would "trade off" such possibilities against alternatives such as additional flow augmentation or higher levels of treatment. In deciding upon the location of a new industrial plant, the firm would consider not only transportation costs and other factors affecting assembly, production, and distribution costs but also the increment of costs (abatement costs and damage costs) of alternative locations. The location producing lowest costs would be the one at which the marginal costs of the alternatives bearing upon over-all costs are equalized.

While the point is expanded later, it is worth noting that the firm "internalizes" all these costs. A water resources authority in a basin does not internalize all of them, and consequently it must attempt to have the opportunity costs of water resources use, including waste disposal, reflected in the decisions of entities which are simultaneously considering other resources costs.

The firm's general objective is to maximize profits, which implies that the costs associated with waste disposal will be minimized at the profit-maximizing level of output. If, for example, the firm could lower its costs by doing a little less effluent treatment and permitting a little more damage, or by doing a little more water treatment and a little less recovery of wastes, or a little more augmentation of low flows and a little less temporary storage of wastes, or a bit more process adjustment and a little less direct reaeration of the stream, etc., its over-all profit position could not be at a maximum.

As part of its general profit-maximizing activities, the firm would integrate its waste control activities with other aspects of its water-related operations. In areas where actual depletion of water is not a significant problem the linkage between water quality optimization and other aspects of water development is primarily via the effects of flow regulation.

Thus in computing the costs of alternative water quality control devices, the firm would need to consider complementary and competitive relationships between different water uses and alteration of the stream's flow regimen. Accordingly, flow-augmentation costs would have to be determined in light of the fact that this alternative is ordinarily complementary with navigation, for example, but at least partly competitive with irrigation and flood control. Any net benefits foregone in using flow augmentation to improve water quality in the optimum system are counted among the costs associated with waste disposal. Moreover, the firm would consider the full marginal costs of producing particular products including those costs which are imposed on other activities by waste disposal.

If markets adequately registered the population's evaluation of all goods and services sold by the hypothetical firm, its solution to the waste disposal problem would be "efficient," as that term is understood in economic welfare theory. Consequently, it might be assumed that the appropriate public policy toward waste disposal problems could be inferred directly from the actions of a firm so situated that it bears all waste-disposal costs. Such reasoning helps to establish some points relevant to the determination of appropriate public policy. It is clear, for example, that when public policy explicitly recognizes an area, say, a basin, as an interdependent system (as the hypothetical firm does), the results will tend to be more beneficial than those yielded by a series of independent decisions. Moreover, it becomes apparent that two kinds of problems confront a regional water resources authority. One is the problem of devising an optimum water quality management system in view of all relevant uses of water, and the other is providing for an appropriate distribution of costs and/or other waste discharge regulations among economic units and activities. The "appropriate" distribution of costs is not here viewed as a matter of "equity" but rather as a matter of "efficiency" in resources use. The extremely large potential of industrial process adjustments and waste reclamation practices in reducing waste discharges and the important effect of location decisions on system costs emphasize the importance of cost distribution *as an element of system design* where the final decision on these matters does not fall within the purview of the water resources agency.

ECONOMIC CRITERIA CONSIDERING THE PROBABILISTIC CHARACTER OF COSTS

It may be helpful in visualizing economic criteria for optimum design if some of the concepts are outlined graphically in a highly simplified context. It is assumed that there is a single type of residual waste material which may be either degradable or non-degradable. It is also assumed that the regional authority designs and builds abatement measures, including, say, waste treatment and flow augmentation, but not water treatment plants. It is further assumed that it is possible to estimate damage cost functions which, where appropriate, incorporate the optimal combination of water treatment and value of physical damages ($MC_T = MC_D$). These are henceforth referred to as "damage costs" or simply as damages.

For expositional purposes attention is first directed to an individual outfall. As indicated in some detail in Part II, the discharge of a waste from a given outfall may give rise to costs in a series of downstream uses. Figure 7 shows two hypothetical downstream damage functions $D = f(x)$ where x is the amount of the waste product in the effluent from the outfall. The illustrated damage functions show the incremental decline in the cost of the optimum combination of water supply treatment costs and the value of physical damages for a unit reduction in waste discharge. For each quality of raw water corresponding to a level of upstream waste discharge, the downstream user would have an incentive to combine the alternatives open to him in this way. A is such a function for one downstream point of use;

B is a similar function for another; and the segment $A + B$ shows the two functions added together over the relevant range. It is important to note that A and B are added *vertically*. This is because they represent complementary or serial costs corresponding to a given level of discharge of the waste. For example, for the concentration of the waste corresponding to the level of discharge indicated by point

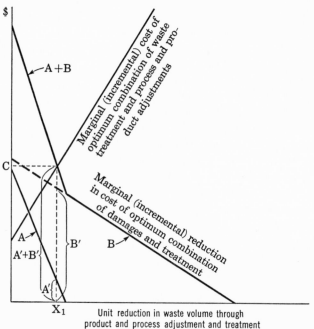

Figure 7.

X_1, incremental damage costs to A are the line segment A', incremental damage costs to B are the line segment B', and over-all incremental damage costs are the two combined, $A' + B'$. In this illustration, non-linear total damage functions are assumed. At later points in the exposition, linear damage functions—giving rise to constant incremental damages—are assumed.

A bit of explanation concerning the derivation of damage functions like A and B may be useful. Due to streamflow variation, downstream damages and water supply treatment costs are necessarily probabilistic rather than deterministic variables. At any given point of use the costs (treatment plus damages) will vary with the streamflow.[4] This is shown for a hypothetical point of use in Figure 8.

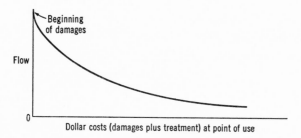

Figure 8.

Figure 9 indicates the probability with which any given level of flow is expected to occur in a given year.

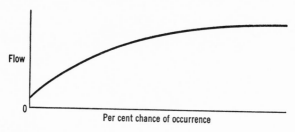

Figure 9.

Figure 10 relates costs at the point of use for a given rate of discharge and corresponding to a given flow to the percentage chance that such a flow will occur in a single year. The expected value (mathematical expectation) of downstream costs is calculated by multiplying the probability of each flow by the corresponding cost (treatment plus damage) and totaling these values. In other words the mathematical expectation of damages associated with a particular level of discharge is the integral of a cost-frequency curve like curve 1 in Figure 10. Assume that the integral of curve 1 represents the expected value of damage costs under conditions of uncontrolled waste

[4] These costs may take a variety of forms. In the case of recreation they would represent willingness to pay for the recreation opportunity foreclosed.

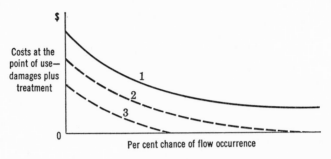

Costs at the point of use—damages plus treatment

1

2

3

0

Per cent chance of flow occurrence

Figure 10.

discharge. Downstream costs averted by reducing residual waste materials in water can then be estimated by constructing a new cost-frequency curve which shows costs at each flow probability after the reduction. Curves 2 and 3 in Figure 9 indicate the situation for a hypothetical case. The difference between the integrals (expected values of the probability distributions) of any two functions is the expected value of the costs avoided at the point of use by the upstream reduction in residual wastes. From a succession of such calculations a curve can be constructed for an expected value of total costs avoided (see Figure 11).

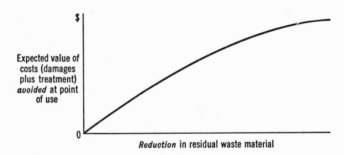

Expected value of costs (damages plus treatment) *avoided* at point of use

0

Reduction in residual waste material

Figure 11.

The curves showing the incremental reduction in cost in Figure 7 can be derived from a total costs-avoided function by taking its first derivative. In other words the incremental curves in Figure 7 represent the slopes of total curves such as shown in Figure 11.

For the purpose of deciding to what extent it would be economically justifiable to institute waste reduction at the outfall, function MC appears in Figure 7. MC represents the incremental cost of instituting optimum waste reduction measures at the outfall.[5] If the relevant alternatives are, say, waste recovery and waste treatment, the function represents incremental costs at points where $MC_R = MC_T$. This might be achieved by direct planning of both treatment and recovery processes by the regional authority, or, if only treatment is directly under the control of the authority, by making sure that the discharging unit views the marginal cost of treatment as an opportunity cost. Under the conditions indicated in Figure 7, abatement measures should be carried to point X_1 in order to achieve minimum total costs.[6] At this point the combined marginal cost of optimum abatement measures at the outfall equals the expected value of damage costs avoided (optimal combination of water supply treatment costs and value of physical damages).[7]

It may be worthwhile restating why point X_1 represents an optimum combination of upstream and downstream measures. At this point a small further increase in abatement activity at the outfall would cost more than the expected value of downstream water treatment costs and damages avoided by the downstream users. The argument is symmetrical for a slight reduction in abatement activity at the outfall.

When costs associated with waste disposal are minimized, the incremental costs associated with waste disposal are equated at each outfall. This means that the marginal costs associated with waste disposal are equalized in all directions. However, it does not mean that the marginal cost of treating will be the same at each outfall along a stream. This would only be the case if downstream costs per unit of waste were equal for different outfalls, as they might be when two outfalls are across the stream from each other; then it would be necessary for cost minimization.

---

[5] These are "long-run" or planning type costs in the economist's terminology.

[6] Since there are scale economies in treatment, sewage collection costs should be incurred until the addition of a marginal unit of collection costs just cancels the reduction of treatment costs.

[7] The same principles would hold for a *stream* treatment plant, i.e., a plant which treats the entire flow of a stream. (See the description of the Emscher plant in chapter 7.) If there are no *uses* of the stream (other than waste disposal) between the point of individual waste discharges and the plant, the analysis is exactly the same.

A special case of some practical importance occurs when successive downstream users are so close together that natural purification effects can be neglected or when wastes are not degradable. In this case, the expected value of marginal downstream costs is higher the farther upstream a waste discharge is made; consequently, cost minimization demands higher marginal abatement costs at outfalls further upstream. This is illustrated in Figure 12 where linear damage functions and no downstream changes in flow are assumed for expository convenience in addition to the assumptions indicated earlier. Constant incremental damages correspond to linear expected total cost (treatment and damages) functions. The X's represent points of water use and effluent outfall. The D's (added vertically as one moves upstream because damages at successive downstream points are additive) represent the expected value of damages per unit of waste discharged into the stream.[8] Given that damages and the abatement measures comprehended in the MCA's are the only alternatives available, costs are minimized when abatement is carried to the X' points. While marginal costs are lower at X'_3 than at X'_2 and X'_1, it is not possible to substitute treatment at outfall X_3 for upstream treatment. Increased treatment at X_3 would simply mean that more costs are incurred than saved.

Conversely, if upstream treatment were substituted for treatment at X_3, higher marginal cost per mg/1 would be incurred. The same analysis holds for each outfall. Hence the costs saved are at a maximum when abatement is carried to points, X'_1, X'_2, and X'_3. Given the alternatives under discussion (which do not include altering the streamflow), a combination of alternatives can in principle be specified which would minimize the expected value of long-term costs. It is notable that this result would tend to occur if each waste discharger had the expected value of damage costs associated with his discharge levied on him.

Let us now assume that it is possible to alter the flow regimen by means of reservoir storage. Determination of the optimum amount of storage can be illustrated by a set of curves closely analogous to those used to illustrate optimum levels of waste discharge reduction.

[8] If variable effluent charges are levied on the firm in accordance with streamflow, in order to maximize profits the firm must compute the expected value of these charges and design its treatment facilities or other abatement measures as indicated in the text.

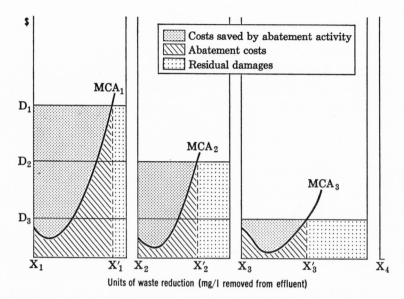

Figure 12.

Consider again a hypothetical streamflow-cost curve. Costs in this case are the total costs for various flow levels of optimal combinations of downstream alternatives—for example, waste treatment, water supply treatment, value of physical damages.

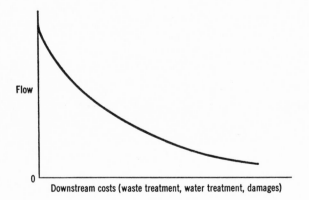

Figure 13.

Given a flow frequency curve such as pictured in Figure 9, one can then straightforwardly proceed to construct a set of curves analogous to those in Figure 10. In this case, however, the downstream costs associated with a given flow remain the same, but flow regulation increases the minimum flow which results from a given set of meteorological conditions. In Figure 10 waste treatment reduced the damage associated with any given flow condition but did not alter its probability of occurrence.

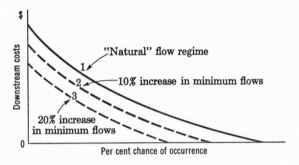

Figure 14.

As before, the integrals of the curves are the expected values of the probability distribution of costs. From a succession of such calculations a total downstream expected value of costs avoided function can be constructed analogous to that shown in Figure 11, but in this case the damage reduction corresponds to increases in minimum flow rather than reduction in residual waste material. A costs-avoided function is illustrated in Figure 15.

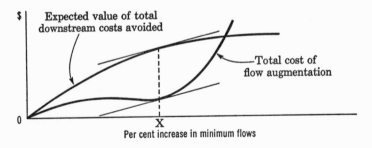

Figure 15.

A total cost function for the storage capacity necessary to produce the increases in minimum flow is also shown in Figure 15. Minimum expected total cost (or maximum expected net benefit if avoided downstream costs are termed benefits) is achieved at an increase in flows corresponding to point X. The slopes of the total storage cost and downstream cost functions are equal to their respective incremental functions. Accordingly at point X the optimality condition (i.e., equality of incremental cost) prevails.[9]

The same solution can readily be stated in terms of functions which are more familiar from previous discussion (see Figure 16).

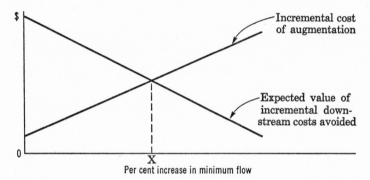

Figure 16.

In general the optimality criterion is that the *expected value* of the incremental costs of all relevant alternatives should be equalized at the margin. If effluent charges are used to control individual waste discharge, this condition requires that such charges reflect the incremental offsite costs imposed by each waste discharge. Charges will of course be lower when the assimilative capacity is increased by flow augmentation. In a correctly designed system the lowered charges reflect a gain in efficiency.

[9] This result may also be stated in terms of the simple calculus. The slopes of the total function are equal to their respective first derivatives. At point X the two derivatives are equal. If we were to construct a total (downstream costs and storage) cost function, the first derivative of that function would be equal to zero at point X, and total costs would accordingly be at a minimum.

HYDROLOGIC VARIABILITY AND
TREATMENT PLANT DESIGN

Hydrologic variability also presents an interesting economic problem in the design of treatment plants. The social costs of a given quantity of a pollutant discharged may be much greater at one time than at another. During periods of high streamflow, waste disposal into the stream is likely to be virtually without downstream damages,[10] and the only justification for operating treatment plants may be the elimination of floating materials which are unsightly and add to the deposition of sludge banks, which may cause problems later.

If a system were designed and operated to achieve cost minimization over time, the costs of its waste treatment plants might well be lower during high flow and considerably higher during low flow than they are now. For one thing, plants would probably be smaller, and during high flow they might cut out their biological sections completely, or in an activated sludge plant cut back considerably on degree of treatment by reducing aeration.[11] During periods of low flow, the plants might rely more heavily on greater aeration and addition of chemicals—measures that are presently considered "supplemental." Functioning in this way would require more precise plant operation than is now typical practice, and the additional costs would have to be weighed against the additional benefits.

Plants are usually designed to achieve lowest cost at an arbitrary and rather extreme design flow which in the United States is normally the seven-day average, once-in-ten-year-probability low streamflow. The plant is then operated in a more or less unchanged fashion even at much higher flows. Long-term costs could probably be reduced by designing a plant that would operate most efficiently at a higher, and

[10] Blair Bower (in correspondence) warns that this is not always the case. "Given a discharge point upstream or an intake or user downstream during high flow periods, travel time is decreased so that BOD may be increased at the downstream point. Kaplovsky found this for the Delaware estuary and I also found a tendency in that direction in the lower Meramec."

[11] A new high-rate activated sludge plant designed to serve a population of 1.1 million at Hamburg, Germany, will cut out the activated sludge stage in the winter. See Daniel A. Okun, "Wastewater Treatment in Europe," *Journal of the Water Pollution Control Federation*, July, 1962, p. 710.

more normal, flow.[12] The added treatment required at low flow might be provided by adding chemicals or stepping up the air input. Operating costs not involving an additional investment can be quite high during the rare periods of extremely low flow and still yield a comparative advantage over additional capital investment.

For example, let us assume that a plant is designed to deal with a low-flow contingency which has a probability of recurrence of once in ten years. Let us further suppose that the probability of this event occurring in any given year is equal to that for any other year. In other words, variation in hydrological events is assumed to be random.

The expected value of the extra cost of dealing with such an extreme low flow can then be treated as an annual average. It is possible to establish how high this annual average can be without its present worth exceeding a dollar of current investment by determining the present worth of a constant expenditure stream of $1.00 per year. The present value of such a perpetuity discounted at 5 per cent annual interest is $20.00.[13] This means that 5 cents could be spent annually, or 50 cents during the once-in-ten-year-probability low flow, and the expected present value of such an expenditure stream would not exceed $1.00. In other words, 50 cents could be spent every 10 years in perpetuity, and the cost would probably be no greater than spending $1.00 for capital equipment now. This means, for example, that if $2 million of the capital value of a large plant is for the purpose of dealing with the once-in-ten-year contingency, $1 million could instead be spent on operating costs every 10 years in perpetuity at no greater expected cost.

It has already been mentioned that methods are available for substantially increasing the performance of treatment plants at the expense

---

[12] For a theoretical discussion of the concept of "flexibility" in plant design, see George Stigler, "Production and Distribution in the Short Run," *Journal of Political Economy*, 47, 1939, reprinted in American Economic Association, *Readings in the Theory of Income Distribution* (Philadelphia: The Blackiston Company, 1949). The virtue of flexibility is recognized, at least to some extent, in turbine design. The turbine is designed to operate most efficiently at the expected "normal operating level." There is a maximum range of heads for which the turbine is designed in the ratio generally of 2 : 1.

[13] The formula for the present value of an annuity of unit value per period for a term of n periods at rate of interest i is as follows:

$$\frac{[1 - (1 + i)^{-n}]}{i}$$

of increased operating costs, and there is evidence that these possibilities have recently increased.

Analogous reasoning indicates the important role which other measures involving low capital investment but high operating costs, such as artificial stream reaeration, would play in a system aimed at achieving lowest costs over time.

Another factor to be considered in achieving an optimum combination of capital and "postponable" operating costs is that the plant is usually built for some projected load, and for some period of time the capacity is greater than needed to achieve the objective. On the other hand "doses" of operating costs will be small at first and can be gradually increased as needed. The discounting process, of course, weighs postponed expenditures less heavily than near-term ones, and this is favorable to alternatives with high operating costs, but is neglected in the example.

EFFLUENT CHARGES AND THE OPTIMAL SYSTEM

Unless *all decisions* bearing upon waste disposal and water use come within the purview of the regional authority, some indirect measures such as charges are needed to achieve the optimal combination of system elements. As stated previously, considerations involved in the use of water resources do not in themselves provide complete criteria for decisions concerning production, production processes, industrial location, etc. For purposes of illustration, presume the authority directly provides only flow augmentation. In this case a system of charges—or a refined system of standards as discussed in chapter 4—will be necessary to produce optimal combinations of treatment, other measures to reduce waste discharge, and damage costs.

Presume that waste dischargers are assessed with the expected value of incremental downstream damages, or alternatively that the agency contemplating flow augmentation calculates the present value of a system of variable effluent charges equal to short-run incremental damages imposed. Flow augmentation should be provided so long as the sum of the costs avoided by an increment of augmentation downstream from the augmentation facility exceeds the cost of providing an increment of flow augmentation.[14] The optimum level of augmentation and other alternatives will not tend to exist unless the marginal cost of reducing the sum of the expected value of incremental damages by flow augmentation is equal to the sum of the marginal costs of reducing damages by discharge point abatement measures optimally distributed in the basin. The latter condition will not be met unless charges levied on individual effluents are equal to the incremental damages they individually impose.[15] The system of charges so arrived at may produce revenue greater or less than that required to cover the average costs (interest, operating, maintenance, and replacement) of providing the flow augmentation facilities. Thus, problems of obtaining additional financing or disposing of surplus funds might exist. Nevertheless, it is a particular merit of the charges system that it provides revenue for the implementation of efficient large-scale measures if such are available.

It is notable that optimum results would not follow if charges were based on a physical criterion such as the quantity of waste discharged. Also it should be pointed out that in principle the regional authority must have information concerning the cost function of all feasible alternatives. Further commentary concerning possible practical approximations requiring less information are discussed below.

"NON-MARKET" SOCIAL GOALS— CONSTRAINTS ON THE OBJECTIVE

The objectives so far suggested as appropriate for public policy would in essence produce the system of water quality management facilities achieved by a competitive firm [16] so situated and integrated as to "internalize" the pollution-caused "externalities." If there were no problems in the manner in which the market registers water quality

---

[14] In multi-unit systems, the problem of optimizing becomes exceedingly complex. Indeed, precise optimization awaits further development of procedures such as those discussed in Maass, *Design of Water Resource Systems, op. cit.*

[15] For a rigorous analysis of an analogous problem involving highway investment and capacity allocation, see Herbert Mohring, "The Benefits of Highway Investment," presented before the Brookings Institution Conference on Government Investment, to be published.

[16] Or one regulated by a public authority on the basis of criteria which would produce competitive market results.

values, this solution would be quite consistent with the general rationale of a market system.

However, public bodies can and should take account of those aspects of water quality for which market evaluations do not presently exist, cannot be imputed, or cannot be accepted. These may include matters such as general environmental effects, public health, and perhaps others. So long as acceptable methodologies for measurement are not available, we may term these "incommensurables."

Methods of Approach

Two ways of handling these incommensurables come to mind. One way would be to label them "intangible" and disregard them in planning and designing optimum waste disposal systems. Then, when the system designs are actually to be considered by representatives of the public, side information could be provided on aesthetic effects, public health, and other matters considered relevant to arriving at a decision in the public interest.

An alternative approach is to include incommensurable goals in the process of system design by expressing them in physical terms and treating them as constraints upon the cost-minimization objective. For example, if social choice should dictate that the oxygen level in a stream must at all times be high enough to support fish life, the system must be designed to minimize the real cost associated with waste disposal subject to the constraint, or "minimum standard," that D.O. is to be kept at a specified level.[17] Conceivably this would require a different combination of units with different operating procedures than a system designed without the standard or constraint. Presuming the constraint is effective and not automatically achieved if costs are minimized, it will increase the cost of the system, the extra cost representing the limitation which the constraint places upon the objective.[18]

[17] See also S. V. Ciriacy-Wantrup, *Resources Conservation* (Berkeley: University of California Press, 1952), chapter 18, where the view is presented that "minimum standards" are a useful device for dealing with uncertainty in the formulation of resources policy.

[18] The distinction between objectives and constraints can be troublesome when "policy" constraints are involved. "Technological" constraints, which set the physical framework within which maximization (or minimization) is carried out, are in principle fairly clear-cut. In a pollution problem such a constraint might be that

Flexibility of the Procedure

Actually constraints upon the objective function need not be limited to those instances where deficiencies in market processes require them. The decision model framework is flexible enough to incorporate any constraints public policy wishes to impose upon the achievement of efficiency, as it has been here defined. Indeed, the objective need not be efficiency at all. For example, the goal of "cleaning up the streams," if its requirements can be made explicit, could be posed to the exclusion of all others, or it could be constrained in various ways. Achieving it would still involve a problem of some interest and significance, since a number of alternative methods could be incorporated into the system design and therefore the problem of "optimum" system design still exists.

It must be said, however, that while this type of framework can be used to combine efficiency and policy goals, the inclusion of policy goals means that the procedure cannot lead to a full optimum but only to a sub-optimum, i.e., an optimum subject to higher-level decisions constraining the minimization (maximization) process.[19]

To be consistent with efforts to achieve maximum welfare, the policy constraints should be considered "provisional," and viewed as subject

water cannot flow uphill. "Policy" constraints however can be viewed as requirements set on certain desirable results which constrain the effort devoted to the attainment of others (objectives)—for example, a minimum D.O. requirement constraining the cost-minimization objective.

As a generalization the following distinction has been proposed. "A practicable distinction between constraints and objectives might go as follows: A requirement is a constraint if (a) it must not be violated at any cost however high or with any probability however low, and (b) if there is no gain or advantage in overfulfilling it. On the other hand, a requirement is one of the objectives of the firm if it can be violated, though at a cost or penalty, or if there is an advantage in overfulfilling it." (Robert Dorfman, "Operations Research," *American Economic Review*, September, 1960, pp. 614–15.) Obviously, policy constraints often do not fully meet the rigorous conditions described, and those set out in a model intended to deal with pollution would have difficulty in doing so; hence the great importance of not considering constraints immutable and of testing the sensitivity of costs to them.

[19] For an interesting and instructive discussion of optima and suboptima, see Charles J. Hitch and Roland N. McKean, *The Economics of Defense in the Nuclear Age* (Cambridge: Harvard University Press, 1960), part II; or for discussion more directly addressing water resources issues, Roland McKean, *Efficiency in Government Through Systems Analysis* (New York: John Wiley & Sons, 1958).

matter for research and study in order to discover how well they represent the preferences of society. One way of studying them from this point of view is to test their cost sensitivity. By varying a constraint by small amounts, redetermining the optimum system, and collating the change in costs with the associated physical changes (i.e., effects on oxygen levels, appearance, aquatic life, etc., in specific stretches of stream), information can be provided which will permit considered choices to be made by representatives of the public. This provides a means of, in a manner of speaking, exploring a collective demand function reflecting the distribution of political power, thus permitting a closer approach to the goal of meeting the preferences of society.

One useful way of stating the results of experiments with the constraints that are not valued directly by, or imputable from, the market is in terms of what they must "at least be worth." For example, a social judgment may be made that algae growth is to be restricted beyond the point indicated by the cost-minimizing solution in order to preserve the appearance of the water. A comparison of the optimum system with and without the constraint will not establish precisely what the avoided destruction of aesthetic pleasure is worth, but it will indicate the *least* value that must be attached to it if the level of control procedures is to be worth while. If constraints are imposed representing goals not directly commensurable with the values stated in monetary terms in the objective function, marginal conditions analogous to those indicated earlier must still hold if the cost-minimization objective is to be fulfilled. The optimum system is not attained until a situation is reached in which it is impossible to make incremental "tradeoffs" between alternatives that will lower costs without violating the constraints. The incremental costs affected by the constraint (say, waste dilution) now, however, contain an imputed element which derives from the limited supply of the constrained input (say, dissolved oxygen).[20]

---

[20] In principle the problem of finding an optimum system under constrained conditions is solvable by the use of differential calculus and the method known as La Grange multipliers. See Alain Enthoven, "The Simple Mathematics of Maximization," an appendix in Hitch and McKean, *op. cit.* When the problem is set up in this form the "multiplier" indicates the marginal cost of the constraint in terms of the costs included in the objective, i.e., an estimate of the cost-saving which would occur if the "standard" or constraint is reduced slightly. The problem can also be set up in the form of a mathematical or linear program. When this is done the so-called "dual" yields an estimate of the incremental cost of the constraints. For

The design of efficient systems and experimentation with the constraints require large amounts of data and extensive knowledge of physical and economic relationships. Rapid and flexible computational techniques could be useful in measuring the physical characteristics of pollution and in working out the actual minimization (maximization) procedure.

Once a combination of system elements has been decided upon it will be necessary to utilize charges, effluent standards, or some other regulation device to achieve optimum waste reduction at individual outfalls. The charge, if a charge is used, must be just high enough to achieve the standard, and it must not be possible to expand the large-scale measures at an incremental cost less than the incremental cost which can be avoided at the individual outfalls. If a number of pollutants are involved, the expected value of all incremental costs avoided by an expansion in the large-scale measures must be added together and compared with the cost of expanding the measure. In the case of some pollutants the incremental cost may include explicitly measurable residual damages.

STREAM SPECIALIZATION TECHNIQUES— CLASSIFICATION AND ZONING

It has been aptly written that "It can in fact be argued that the *chief gain* from systematic analysis is the stimulus that it provides for the

---

examples of the application of programming techniques to water resources planning problems, see Earl O. Heady, "Mathematical Analysis Models for Quantitative Application in Watershed Planning," *Economics of Watershed Planning*, edited by G. S. Tolley and F. E. Riggs (Ames: The Iowa State University Press, 1961), and in the same volume Robert Dorfman, "Mathematical Analysis-Design of the Simple Valley Project." See also Arthur Maass and Maynard M. Hufschmidt, "Report on the Harvard Program of Research in Water Resources Development," *Resources Development—Frontiers for Research* (Boulder: University of Colorado Press, 1960); and *Design of Water Resource Systems, op. cit.*

Prior to application of such methods, the objectives together with relevant constraints are set down in the form of an "objective function." This function has been described in the text and may be summarized as follows: The objective is to minimize the sum of the costs of all water quality management alternatives, including the value of physical damages, given certain constraints. Some of the latter may represent goals which are not directly commensurable with the objective; others represent objective technical circumstances which constrain the achievement of the objective.

invention of better systems." [21] Thus far the present discussion has pro-
ceeded in terms of the optimal design of a single system with a single
set of constraints and given pollution loads at given points. Actually an
arbitrary judgment that an entire basin or other water resources area
should be approached in this fashion may prejudge certain values that
would be better considered as variables in the analysis. For example,
if the maintenance of fish habitat for sport fishing is a valuable undertaking in a particular sub-basin, or in a particular stretch of stream,
specialization may permit a lower real cost associated with waste
disposal (including, of course, foregone recreational opportunities)
than would be the case if conditions suitable for sport fish culture were
maintained throughout the basin.

Advantages of Specialization

The designation of certain streams or stretches of streams—either by
strictly enforced stream standards or explicit zoning—for use primarily
for recreation and others primarily for the disposal of wastes, does
appear to have some technical and economic rationale.

The specialized use of watercourses has notable advantage for
recreation, since the value of a stream for recreation depends in part
upon the scenic beauty and the "naturalness" of the environment. Not
only can these aspects be marred by spillovers or external effects of
industrial or other developments, but even highly treated wastes may
leave residuals, such as plant nutrients, which can detract from recreation value.

Advantages also accrue to waste disposal when it is the primary use.
The rate at which water absorbs oxygen from the atmosphere is directly
proportional to the oxygen deficit (the amount by which dissolved
oxygen falls short of saturation). Hence, the lower the dissolved oxygen
falls, the greater the rate of atmospheric reaeration. Accordingly, a
body of water in which dissolved oxygen is almost depleted can assimilate large amounts of oxygen-demanding wastes while still maintaining
aerobic conditions. In addition, industrial producers can take advantage
of a stream's self-purification capacity, and as a group they may find it
less costly to treat intake water, the major part of which is for cooling,

[21] Hitch and McKean, *op. cit.*, p. 187; emphasis in the original.

than to provide extensive treatment of wastes. Moreover, intake water may be obtained from another basin, and the contiguous stream used for the single purpose of waste disposal. (The single-purpose use of the Emscher River is described in chapter 7.)

Plant nutrients can play a somewhat different role in a stream used for waste disposal than in one devoted primarily to recreation and public water supplies. In the latter, taste, odor, and treatment problems presented by algae might well necessitate expensive measures such as tertiary treatment of wastes or land disposal techniques. However, when waste disposal is the main use the presence of nitrates in effluents can be beneficial. Should the oxygen content become exhausted as a result of heavy organic pollution, nitrates provide a reserve of oxygen which can be utilized by bacteria, thus preventing septic conditions and attendant odor nuisances. Indeed, during the summer months sodium nitrate is sometimes added to streams to prevent the generation of offensive odors.[22]

It should be recognized that the specialized use of streams can create problems as well as offer advantages, and care must be taken in specifying zones where waste disposal is to be the primary use. Unless this is done, downstream values may be adversely affected to such an extent as to nullify any advantages of specialization.

Methods of Analysis

If all relevant values could be measured by a monetary standard, a variety of situations utilizing differing standards for different streams or stretches of stream might be explored in order to approach an optimum system. For example, the value of recreation lost in a stretch of stream, minus the increment due to more specialized recreation use of certain waters, would be computed and weighed against the reduction in waste disposal costs. Again, the appropriate criterion for cost minimization would be equalization of these costs at the margin. In following this procedure, cognizance would have to be taken of special advantages of location for certain industries. For example, in computing

[22] For a defense of nitrates in effluents delivered into streams heavily loaded with municipal and industrial wastes, see Louis Klein, *Aspects of River Pollution* (New York: Academic Press, Inc., 1957), chapter 14.

the costs of maintaining a stream for recreational purposes it is necessary to include the higher treatment costs of industries located there and the higher costs or less desirable location of prospective industries. In a case of this kind, it would be extremely easy to neglect "spillovers" or external diseconomies. Such diseconomies may take the form not only of fairly immediate, albeit indirect, costs, but also of inflexibilities in future stream use imposed by stream classification or zoning.

Again, many of the costs relevant in determining an optimal location pattern for industry lie outside the jurisdiction of a water resources authority. This suggests that there would be merit in the use of differential charges to induce the desired locational pattern rather than absolute prohibition of certain locations. Thus low charges would represent the advantage of compact development and low-cost waste disposal, including scale economies in treatment, in an area to be used specifically for waste disposal. High charges would reflect the disadvantages of scattered development and interference with recreational values in other areas. This would permit firms or municipalities to discharge into an area of high recreational value if they find this very advantageous in terms of their own direct costs. If the charges are approximately right, discharge into such an area would mean that the high value increment of recreation opportunity lost was in fact less valuable than the value of the resources needed to preserve it.

"Across the board" regulatory procedures may well establish a pattern of universal mediocrity of streams. None are really bad, but none are really good either. Also, such regulation does not provide an incentive for compact industrial development and therefore reduces the opportunities for achieving scale economies. Consequently, it would appear to be important that studies of the possible advantages of stream specialization be conducted in all basins.

One might expect a pattern of specialization to establish itself if each industry were always charged (or paid) a sum equal to its marginal cost to the regional water system. In areas where industry is already established in a pattern which *de facto* produces more or less specialized streamflow, this pattern would be encouraged by the institution of effluent charges based on short-run incremental social costs. Low effluent charges would provide an incentive to locate on certain streams, and rising land values would encourage compact development. Accordingly, a kind of "natural zoning" would occur.

This pattern might not become established, however, in areas of new development. If, for example, one starts with a clean stream, effluent charges based on current social costs will increase as industrial and municipal development takes place. Incremental social costs are low as long as dilution and degradation capacity are high, but they increase as other water uses are seriously infringed upon. Consequently, charges might encourage scattered development by giving each waste discharger an incentive to separate his discharge from points of use. This incentive would continue as long as all stretches of the stream continued to be used for multiple purposes. However, if explicit system design analyses suggest substantial advantages from specialized use, promotional effluent charges lower than current incremental offsite costs and/or explicit zoning may well produce the lower cost system by helping to provide compact development along the specialized stretches of stream.

If some kinds of recreation or any public goal cannot be valued explicitly but their physical requirements must be viewed as constraints, an analogous type of analysis may still be useful. Various stream specialization possibilities can be explored, and the decision as to whether the public interest is adequately protected can be left to representatives of the public. If the measurable real cost of scheme I, for example, is $1 million less than the cost of scheme II, which uses stream specialization, society may choose scheme I even though some unknown (but implicitly less than $1 million) value of recreation opportunities is foregone. Effective decisions would still be dependent upon accurate description of relevant variables not directly commensurable with the objective such as the physical effects of the plans and their impact upon, say, the rate of use of recreation facilities.

One particular pattern of some interest develops when a tributary is used primarily or solely for waste disposal and empties into a main stem used for multiple purposes. In this instance a treatment plant might be constructed at the mouth of the tributary to treat its entire flow. The appropriate degree of treatment would be that which equated the marginal cost of treatment with marginal downstream costs (or met a downstream "standard"). The cost distribution system would then allocate treatment costs to each effluent discharger in accordance with a criterion of his responsibility for them. Also each discharger would be charged with the incremental damage costs (if any) that his waste discharges impose along the tributary. Moreover, there may be a "constraint" that requires the tributary to be kept aerobic. This combination of circumstances would probably produce a situation in which the tributary itself is given far-reaching treatment and effluents at some or all of the outfalls are given a modest amount of treatment. An actual situation of this kind is described in the next chapter, which discusses water management in the Ruhr.

It should once again be noted that the effluent charges are imposed not as a matter of equity but to induce process and product adjustments and perhaps treatment that will minimize the cost of obtaining optimum water quality downstream. By the same token, the waste discharger should be charged no more than is necessary to accomplish this objective, since this would consume more resources than are needed to maintain the tributary at an optimal level of quality for its specialized purpose.

SOME "SHORT-RUN" ASPECTS OF SYSTEM OPERATION AND COST ASSESSMENT

At this point it is useful to introduce a distinction between "long-run" or "planning" costs and "short-run" or "operating" costs. There are two reasons for making this distinction in the present context: (1) An existing system should be operated on the basis of its "current" opportunity costs. This is especially important when certain system elements such as dams must be introduced in "chunks" which are not efficiently divisible. (2) The fact that hydrologic fluctuation may make it desirable that the system of abatement facilities be operated in a variable manner and that waste loads be varied to conform with variations in streamflow suggests the possible desirability of basing effluent charges on short-term variations in cost.

Some General Principles

So far the discussion has been in terms of planning the system, and the concept of costs used has accordingly been one appropriate to the problem of choosing among alternatives not yet being utilized. In other words, the general alternatives which could be brought into play were not assumed to be fixed by past decisions. The view taken was sufficiently long run, for example, to permit the building of dams *instead of* treatment plants. For planning, these are valid and appropriate concepts.

From the short-run point of view of operating a system, however, some types of costs which influence decisions in the initial selection of alternatives are irrelevant. The point has been made several times that if the objective is to minimize the value of resources used to achieve an objective, the cost relevant for choosing a particular method of gaining the objective is the value of the opportunities that must be foregone if the method is chosen. This concept of "opportunity" costs has been used throughout, and methods of producing a better reflection of the value of foregone opportunities to society in decisions with respect to waste disposal was the subject of Part II.

The *concept* that costs represent foregone opportunities does not change once a particular set of facilities has been decided upon and installed, but the *character* of the opportunities foregone does. When a dam is in the planning stage, all the labor, cement, steel, etc., needed for its construction can still be used in other activities and should be used for the dam only if the return is higher in that purpose than in any other feasible alternative. Once the labor, cement, etc., have been embodied in a dam they can no longer be used for alternative purposes, and the price paid for them can no longer be said to represent the value of foregone opportunities.[23] The only costs that are still opportunity costs—and thus relevant for further decisions—are those arising from the operation of the dam for a particular purpose. If the dam is multipurpose, the opportunity costs are "internal," representing the net

[23] See chapter 4 for an explanation of why the price of resources to be used in a certain course of action may usually be considered to reflect the social value of foregone opportunities.

value of the other uses foregone when the dam is used for only one particular purpose.

For purposes of planning waste disposal systems, therefore, the definition of costs properly includes all capital costs of new facilities. The system of abatement should be expanded to the point where an *additional unit* of optimal abatement measures for any given pollutant —or, if the abatement activity involves joint products, for any given combination of pollutants—raises total abatement costs as much as it diminishes pollution damages. If there is a constraint, the system should be expanded until the constraint is met and the marginal total cost of all alternative measures for achieving the constraint are equalized.

However, at any given time after an abatement system is established, only currently variable costs and opportunity costs internal to a multipurpose system are relevant. It has been aptly said that in the economic calculus "bygones are forever bygones." For example, assume that a sewage treatment plant has been designed with greatly "excessive" capacity. In deciding whether to replace this plant with a smaller one, comparison of total costs (including capital costs of both plants) would almost certainly lead to the wrong conclusion. If the original plant has no alternative use—which is probably the case—only its operating costs are relevant in comparison with the new plant. There may be alternative uses for part of the existing investment—for example, the land on which the plant is located. The value of such uses must, of course, be brought into the comparison since they represent genuine opportunity costs. The test is always whether there are currently feasible, valuable alternatives. From the point of view of allocating resources to their most productive use, only inputs which have alternative uses can be said to involve costs.

Since storage reservoirs ordinarily cannot be economically constructed in such a way as to add small increments to system capacity, a system adjusting to changing waste load conditions will have periods of excess capacity.[24] Under these circumstances the short-run opportunity costs of using the reservoir for flow augmentation must be compared with alternatives. Appropriate operating procedures of the sys-

[24] For a formal analysis of the considerations governing the optimum timing of the addition of system elements to a system serving expanding demands see *Design of Water Resource Systems, op. cit.,* chapter 2.

tem would be based upon relative marginal operating costs; reliance upon flow augmentation would be heavier, and effluent charges or standards would accordingly be lower, in the earlier period after the dam was built than in the later period. Optimum sequences of abatement facilities construction would vary depending upon relative costs. In a basin starting with low waste loads an initial step might be the construction of primary treatment at some or all outfalls. As waste loads grow, the addition of some reservoir storage at the best sites might become appropriate on cost-minimizing principles. Then with further development of the basin, rising damages plus higher reservoir costs (increasingly valuable alternative use opportunities) might justify higher effluent charges or standards and correspondingly higher levels of waste reduction activities at some outfalls. Rising costs (abatement and residual damages) at some further point might make another dam appropriate. When such a dam is built, a period of distinctly lower operating costs would be encountered, together with lower effluent charges and operating adjustments in existing treatment and waste reduction facilities. Again, the current alternative cost of the resources used would be indicated by current marginal opportunity costs.[25]

Hydrologic Variability and Effluent Charges

Streamflow variation over time presents problems in system design and in the operation of the various system elements in such a way as to minimize costs over time. Aspects of the design problem have been discussed previously. As a generalization, it might be said that the design problem is one of assuring that the scale of the system is properly suited to deal with the expected value of losses imposed by water quality deterioration due to longer term variations in flow. The operating problem is one of continuously adapting the opportunity costs incurred in abatement measures to opportunity costs resulting from variation in damages attendant on changes in the variables affecting the system. Among the most important (if not *the* most important) of

[25] Objections have been made to such large-scale shifts in prices on the part of utility-type enterprises because of the uncertainty they may induce. For divergent views see J. Hirshleifer, "Peak Loads and Efficient Pricing: Comment," *Quarterly Journal of Economics*, 1958; and M. Boiteux, "Peak Load Pricing," *Journal of Business*, April, 1960.

these is variation in streamflow, both seasonal and longer term.

The point has already been made that the costs associated with waste disposal vary strongly over time. This is clearly true of damages. The concentration of pollutants rises during low-flow periods, and increases the likelihood of fish kills, higher water treatment costs, damaging effects associated with salinity and hardness, and, in waters extremely heavily loaded with organic pollutants, anaerobic nuisance conditions. The current opportunity costs of operating a quality control system in an optimal fashion also rise during such periods, when it may be necessary to add chemicals to aid precipitation in treatment plants, to step up the aeration rates in activated sludge plants, to use power turbines and other devices to increase reaeration of the stream, and to augment low flows by reservoir releases. There might be little out-of-pocket operating cost in reservoir releases, but the costs of foregone opportunities will rise if there are substitute uses for the water. The costs may be foregone valuable peak power which could have been generated, or lost recreation opportunities due to drawdown of the reservoir. On the other hand, the reservoir releases may benefit water uses complementary with waste dilution (navigation, for example).

In many instances, manufacturers can economically change the amount and/or quality of waste discharge over short periods of time by temporary withholding of wastes in lagoons or by slowdown or shutdown of production during periods of low flow. Incentives should be provided for the optimal use of these and other measures for altering the pattern of discharges.

These considerations clearly show the important role which forecasting stream conditions and automatic monitoring devices could play in the operation of a system. An essential element in such a procedure would be effluent charges or other measures to regulate individual waste discharges which more or less continuously reflect the marginal costs of each major discharge in view of the objectives and constraints of the system.

CONCLUDING COMMENTS

Part II was devoted primarily to the problem of remedying pollution-caused distortions of cost in situations where no significant economies could be achieved in the collective design and operation of abatement measures. Part III is devoted to problems of designing and operating a system for waste disposal and water supply in instances where collective facilities for regulating quality can provide significant economies. This chapter has focused on the co-ordinate planning of various types of treatment and flow regulation, the incorporation of "incommensurable" social goals into the plan, possible economies achievable by specialized rather than multiple-purpose use of streams, and some special economic problems which stem from hydrologic variability. Attention was directed to the important role that can be played by effluent charges—either alone or in conjunction with other measures for regulating discharge—in a regional system for waste disposal and water supply. The emphasis was not upon equity but upon the role of effluent charges in articulating the decisions that might best be under the direct control of a water resources authority with those that are properly left in the hands of individuals, firms, communities, and public authorities with responsibility for land-use planning. In addition, it was pointed out that the assessment of charges is important in financing the collective features of a system.

It has been noted that, ideally, system planning would consider all alternative uses of water, including its use for waste disposal, the effects of the various uses on water quality, the losses imposed on other uses by quality deterioration, and the value of water-derivative uses. All feasible alternative system designs and operating procedures would be considered, and a solution would be derived which would indicate the optimum combination of system elements and operating procedures in light of the objectives and constraints relevant to the system. There are good reasons, aside from the inherent complexity of the problem and the primitive state or absence of much of the required data, why an optimum solution cannot be fully attained. Inevitable arbitrariness in the specification of constraints, the absence of fully satisfactory means of introducing risk preferences, the uncertainty involved in forecasting future economic variables, as well as extremes in hydrology, militate against the achievement of fully optimum decisions.

It is therefore important to stress that we are still in a situation where a premium must be placed on ingenious simplification which will permit workable procedures to be developed and investigations to be mounted which will achieve satisfactory if not totally precise results.

Nevertheless, an approach of the general type outlined in this chapter appears likely to improve decisions on water quality management. This approach emphasizes the importance of identifying interdependencies and viewing areas and economic functions tied together by "spillovers" in a "system" context; stresses the identification and quantification of alternatives and their systematic testing in light of criteria of merit developed in terms of the objective or objectives of the system; and endeavors to cause the opportunity costs of water resources use to be adequately reflected in decisions not controlled directly by the water resources authority.

These features of the analysis of the water quality problem represent a way of thinking about the problem; they do not imply a specific procedure for solving it. When the situation is a complex one involving numerous alternatives and constraints, optimization procedures applied to formal mathematical models, often with the aid of computers, can be very helpful. However, the major gains from viewing the problem in a "system" context may often be realized by rather rough-and-ready procedures.

In addition, setting out basin-wide pollution control problems in comparatively systematic terms may have useful side effects. For one thing it requires an explicit and unambiguous statement of objectives. Moreover, the need to determine relevant relations and quantify them can play an important part in revealing inadequacies in information. Consequently, potentially fruitful avenues of research may be revealed.

APPENDIX TO CHAPTER 6

A Note on Benefit-Cost Analysis and the "Constrained Cost Minimization" Framework

For those who are familiar with "benefit-cost analysis," it may be useful to restate the "constrained cost minimization" framework, outlined in this chapter, in terms of benefits and costs. Those results of a planned system of waste disposal which can be thought of as reduced damages adequately valued by market-based calculations, may be treated as benefits with which the costs (construction and operation of structures) can be compared. If all pollution effects can be adequately valued, the benefit-cost relationship has its conventional meaning, and the minimization of the real costs of waste disposal is formally identical with maximization of the positive difference between benefits and costs. If constraints are admitted, they must be viewed as objectives or requirements which must be attained. The objective of cost minimization may then be alternatively stated as being the maximization of the positive difference between benefits and costs or the minimization of the negative difference, whichever is appropriate, provided that the requirements of the constraints are met. It may be that a particular system cannot be carried to larger scale than required by the constraints without decreasing net benefits (or increasing net losses), or, what is the same thing, increasing the total costs associated with waste disposal (costs of abatement plus damages). If total costs continue to decline (equivalently if net benefits continue to increase or net "losses" continue to diminish), this means that the marginal product of investment in abatement is positive. Since calculable pollution damage takes a number of forms some of which may be associated with the characteristics to which constraints are applied and some not, it would be quite possible for the over-all benefits (as defined above) to be exceeded by the over-all costs of an abatement system even though the marginal relationship for certain abatement measures is the reverse. In this case the negative net benefits cannot, of course, be taken to indicate an inefficient or undesirable project. The relevant questions are: (1) are the constraints met, and (2) does it pay to contrive to invest in abatement after the constraints are met, i.e., is the marginal efficiency of investment positive? In other words, once constraints are set by social policy, the best system may be viewed as one that meets them at minimum cost and continues to expand individual elements as long as a marginal net benefit is associated with them. In those instances where a constraint is applied to a stream or water supply quality characteristic (say, for public health reasons), the improvement of which can profitably be carried beyond the point required, because it (say) reduces corrosion damage, the constraint will not be effective in an optimum abatement system.

In part, a negative average relationship between benefits and costs may represent neglect of infra-marginal benefits when constraints are used. For example, a limit on bacterial content of drinking water may be set sufficiently high so that further investments in reducing bacteria count would be very costly relative to the added productivity or reduced medical costs it would elicit. On the other hand, the average benefits of this character, due to the reduction of bacteria in drinking water, may be a large multiple of the costs. However, in deciding whether to expand investment such infra-marginal benefits are, of course, irrelevant.

In practice formal benefit-cost analyses of water quality improvement have been limited to the evaluation of low-flow augmentation with water supply and sewage treatment usually the only alternatives considered. In federal agency evaluations industrial and navigation benefits have been calculated in terms of avoided costs, and benefits to public water supplies have been similarly obtained. However, the latter category of benefits differs from those attributable to industrial treatment costs (and those which could, under the appropriate circumstances, be attributed to agriculture and conceivably to recreation), in that they are, to a large degree, not a representation or an imputation of market type valuation. They differ also from benefits determined for power and navigation in multi-purpose projects, where alternative costs are usually used as measures of benefit, in that the latter evaluations presuppose an existing or developable market demand which can be met more cheaply by the use of public capital.

To the extent that public supplies are treated for hardness, corrosiveness, and potability, and such treatment costs are avoided, market type benefits can accrue although decisions on these types of treatment are likely themselves to have been made without much analysis of costs and benefits. On the other hand, public health considerations—which are inevitably a factor in the treatment of public supplies—are in a different category. In their case alternative treatment costs are really a sort of "stand-in" for drinking water standards which are not based upon market valuations.

A similar point may be made in regard to pollution abatement benefits, which are figured as the reduced cost of sewage treatment beyond the primary level, or on other occasions as the alternative cost of a single-purpose flow augmentation facility rather than inclusion of an augmentation feature in a multipurpose facility, and which have bulked large in a number of evaluations. (See, for example, *Allegheny River Reservoir Benefits Resulting from Low Flow Regulation of the Pro-*

posed Allegheny Reservoir, U.S. Public Health Service, Robert A. Taft Sanitary Engineering Center, Cincinnati, July, 1957; and *Potomac River Basin Report,* U.S. Army Engineer District, Baltimore, February, 1963.) These benefits are also not based in any direct fashion upon market valuations but really relate to the achievement of certain receiving water standards. These standards may be derived from recreational, aesthetic, or public health considerations. More often they do not arise from explicit analysis of particular situations but are based on conventional standards and design flows. The advantage of the formulation in the text is not that it avoids such externally imposed standards but that it clearly distinguishes them from market-type benefits while the federal agency practice does not. The latter, by an alternative cost calculation, arbitrarily transposes a "policy" type requirement into a "benefit." In recent multipurpose projects, flow augmentation benefits have been figured as the alternative cost of providing the same enhancement of low flow by means of a single-purpose project.

The major advantage of the constrained objective function formulation is that it avoids this type of obfuscation and puts the problem into a form in which the effects of the constraints can be conveniently analyzed.

7

Water Management in the Ruhr—
A Case Study of the Genossenschaften

~~~~~~

This chapter presents a case study of the design and operation of an existing regional system of water resources management primarily directed toward the problems of waste disposal. The subjects of the study are several German water resources associations operating in the Ruhr industrial area. These are co-operative associations generally referred to as *Genossenschaften*. The small streams of the Ruhr not only support a tremendous industrial development and a massive population, but they do so while providing a generally high level of amenities and recreational opportunity. The *Genossenschaften* of the Ruhr area are the only organizations in the world that have designed, built, and operated *regional* systems for waste disposal and water supply. Of equal interest, they have developed comparatively sophisticated methods of distributing the costs of their operations by levying charges on the effluents discharged in their respective regions. The important role which such charges can play in attaining efficient systems has been indicated in the previous chapters. In this chapter the activities of these organizations are studied in terms of the economic concepts and criteria developed in this study.

One warning must be given before the following sections are read. The emphasis upon principles and generalization lends a false air of precision to the design operation and cost assessment procedures described. Any institution that depends in some measure upon voluntary compliance must frequently accept compromises in order to remain viable. Moreover, even general principles are not always well articulated or fully agreed upon within an organization. Consequently, the following exposition must be viewed as offering generalizations, and the reader must be aware that many exceptions and qualifications go unstated.

GENERAL BACKGROUND AND SUMMARY OF SYSTEM DESIGN ELEMENTS

In this brief introduction to the nature and works of the German water resources *Genossenschaften*, comparatively little is said about the details of their history and legal character. Published descriptions of these aspects are available.[1]

There are eight large water resources *Genossenschaften* in the highly industrialized and heavily populated area generally known as the Ruhr: the Ruhrverband, the Emschergenossenschaft, the Ruhrtalsperrenverein, the Lippeverband, the Wupperverband, the Niersverband, the Linksniederrheinische-Enterwaesserungsgenossenschaft (Lineg), and the Erftverband. These organizations were created by special legislation in the period from 1904 to 1958.[2] There are thousands of water *Genossenschaften* in Germany, most of them created for special

[1] The only general description in English known to the author is Gordon M. Fair, "Pollution Abatement in the Ruhr District," in Henry Jarrett, Ed., *Comparisons in Resource Management* (Baltimore: The Johns Hopkins Press, for Resources for the Future, Inc., 1961). Certain aspects of the work of the *Genossenschaften* are briefly described in S. V. Ciriacy-Wantrup, "Water Quality, A Problem for the Economist," *Journal of Farm Economics*, December, 1961. There is a vast German literature on the *Genossenschaften*. General treatments include Helmut Moehle, "Wasserwirtschaftliche Probleme an Industriefluessen" (Problems of Water Management on Industrial Streams), *Die Wasserwirtschaft*, Vol. 45, No. 4, 1954. *Fuenfzig Jahre Emschergenossenschaft 1906–1956* (Fifty Years of the Emschergenossenschaft), Selbstverlag der Emschergenossenschaft, Essen, 1957. E. H. Max Pruess, "Der Ruhrverband und Ruhrtalsperrenverein als Muster gemeinwirtschaftlicher Wasserwirtschaft" (The Ruhrverband and Ruhrtalsperrenverein as a Pattern for Collective Water Economics), *Staedtehygiene*, Heft 9, 1954. H. W. Koenig, "Wasserverbaende als rationelle Loesung fuer den Gewaesserschutz" (The Water Association as a Rational Solution for Protection of Water Supplies), *Plan— Schweizerische Zeitschrift fuer Landes-, Regional-und Ortsplanung*, Zuerich, September/October, 1960, p. 157. *Wasserwirtschaft in Nordrhein-Westfalen* (Water Economics in Northrhine Westphalia) (Frankfurt/Main: Verwaltungsverlag Gmbh, 1960).

[2] All but one of the *Genossenschaften* were established before 1930. The Erftverband (Verband and Genossenschaft are used interchangeably) was created in 1958 primarily to deal with problems resulting from a massive pumping down of ground water tables in the Erft basin by the coal industry.

purposes such as the drainage or flood protection of specific and limited plots of land. The large *Genossenschaften* in the Ruhr, however, were given almost complete multipurpose authority over water quantity and quality in entire watersheds by their special laws. These organizations are henceforth referred to simply as the *Genossenschaften*. For almost 60 years they have made and executed comprehensive plans for waste disposal, water supply, and flood control, as well as for land drainage, which is a problem of great significance in the coal-mining areas. This has involved the design and construction of a large array of quality management facilities, including large-scale measures of various types and most of the conventional waste-water treatment plants in the region. The *Genossenschaften* are comparable to co-operatives in the Anglo-American sense, but voting power is distributed in accordance with the size of the contribution to an association's expenses, and membership is compulsory. Members of the associations are principally the municipal and rural administrative districts, coal mines, and industrial enterprises.

General public supervision is in the hands of the Ministry of Food, Agriculture, and Forestry of the State of North-Rhine Westphalia in which the *Genossenschaften* are located. The Ministry's supervision is, however, almost completely limited to seeing that the associations comply with the provisions of their constitutions.

The *Genossenschaften* have the authority to plan and construct facilities for water resources management and to assess their members with the cost of constructing and operating such facilities. A process of internal appeal to special boards and of final appeal to the federal administrative courts is available to the individual members.

The statutes creating the *Genossenschaften* set forth the goals and responsibilities of these organizations in highly general terms. This has left the staffs and the members comparatively free to adapt to changing conditions and to develop procedures and concepts in line with experience. One general provision of the statutes has played a large role in successful and efficient operation. This provision specifies that the costs of constructing and operating the system are to be paid by those members who are responsible for them and by those who benefit. Over the years, comparatively elaborate procedures have been developed for assessing the costs of land drainage and waste disposal.

The Ruhr area is one of the most concentrated industrial areas in the entire world. It contains some 40 per cent of total West German industrial capacity and between 75 and 90 per cent of West German production of coal, coke, iron, and steel. There are some 8 million people in the Ruhr's 4,300 square miles—roughly one-half the size of the Potomac River watershed in the United States.

Water resources are extremely limited if one excludes the Rhine River, into which the streams of the Ruhr area flow. Although the Rhine has a mean flow roughly like that of the Ohio, it is drawn upon to supply water to the Ruhr area only during periods of extreme low flow. Not only is the Rhine itself of very poor quality at the point where the Ruhr enters it, but the water from the Rhine must be *lifted* into the industrial area. With present installations, it is possible to "back-pump" the Ruhr as far up as Essen by means of pump stations installed in dams creating a series of shallow reservoirs in the Ruhr. Back-pumping was carried on during the extreme drought of 1959. Development of a large new reservoir for the augmentation of low flows by the Ruhrtalsperrenverein will even further reduce the already modest dependence of the area on the use of Rhine water.

The Ruhr area is much more dependent upon the Rhine for its waste carriage capacity. A large proportion of the wastes discharged from the industrial region into the Rhine now receive comparatively little treatment. However, after construction of a large new biological treatment plant on the Emscher, virtually all effluents reaching the Rhine will have been given far-reaching treatment, and the contribution of this area to the pollution of the Rhine will be comparatively modest.

Five small rivers constitute the water supply and the water-borne waste carriage and assimilative capacity of the industrial area proper. In descending order of size, these are the Ruhr, Lippe, Wupper, Emscher, and the Niers. Their combined *annual* average low flow is only about one fourth of the *low flow of record* on the Delaware River near Trenton, New Jersey, or about one-half of the *low flow of record* on the Potomac River near Washington, D.C.

The amazing waste load which these rivers carry is indicated by the fact that the annual average natural low flow in the Ruhr, which is heavily used for household and industrial water supply and recreation, is less than the volume of effluent discharged into the river. A frequently used rule of thumb is that a river must have at least 8 parts of dilution flow for each part of treated waste discharge if it is to be suitable for reuse.[3]

The *Genossenschaften* have made this small supply of water serve the needs of the mines, factories, and households of the great industrial complex, while permitting the use of streams for recreation and waste disposal. And they have achieved this at relatively modest cost. Despite rather impressive attention to amenities and recreation, the combined expenditure of the *Genossenschaften* on building and operating all waste water treatment plants, dams, pump stations, etc., amounts to about $60 million a year, somewhat over half of which is for land drainage. The largest waterworks in the area is a profit-making enterprise which delivers water for household use at 30 cents per thousand gallons and for industrial use at 20 cents per thousand gallons. These are among the lowest water prices in any of the German metropolitan areas, despite the fact that the waterworks pays a share of regional water supply and quality improvement costs.[4]

The success of the *Genossenschaften* stems from the design and operation of an efficient system. Because of the regional purview of the associations and the dense development of the area, far-reaching use is made of collective abatement measures and stream specialization. Moreover, as will be seen later, so-called indirect measures such as waste reclamation and process engineering play a large role in controlling the generation of industrial wastes.

In the present discussion, references to the *Genossenschaften* may be taken to mean either the Ruhrverband-Ruhrtalsperrenverein or the Emschergenossenschaft-Lippeverband unless a specific organization is indicated. Nominally four organizations, they are linked in two pairs, each under a single management. These are by far the largest *Genossenschaften,* and they have both the most complex physical water resource systems and the most sophisticated methods of assessing costs.

The physical features of the regional system of waste disposal estab-

[3] This was originally proposed by the Royal Commission on Sewage Effluents in England. See Louis Klein, *Aspects of River Pollution* (New York: Academic Press, Inc., 1957), p. 551.

[4] See George Mueller and Franz-Josef Hessing, *Kostentraeger der Wasserversorgung und Abwasserbeseitigung,* Institut fuer Raumforschung (Bad Godesberg: 1962), p. 137.

lished by these organizations are interesting, but only a few general comments are made about them here, since the individual elements involve no technological principles that are not fairly well known to sanitary engineering practice in all developed countries.

Figure 17. River basins of the Ruhr district.

The most important and impressive aspects of the *Genossenschaften* are economic and institutional in character. Although little or no explicit attention was given to formal optimizing procedures, the systems were designed with the explicit objective of minimizing costs of attaining certain standards in the rivers, and there was explicit recognition of the role played by the equi-marginal principle in achieving minimum costs. Perhaps most important, the *Genossenschaften* provide an institution within which a wide range of relevant alternatives can be systematically examined. This even extends to the use of legislation, as illustrated by the recent German law forbidding the sale of "hard" detergents after October, 1964. Cost assessment of alternative methods of dealing with detergents was primarily carried out in the laboratories of the *Genossenschaften*.[5]

In the Ruhr River Basin itself the general objective of the system is to maintain water quality suitable for water supply and recreation.[6] In the Lippe the objective is much the same; the Lippe, however, is made largely unsuitable for drinking purposes by salinity arising both from natural sources and from the saline water pumped from coal mines. Some of the tributaries of the Lippe, notably the Stever and the Muehlenbach, are used for potable supply. The Emscher, by far the smallest of the three major streams, is used exclusively for waste dilution, degradation, and carriage. Actually, as an aid to protecting the quality of the Ruhr, a small portion of the wastes generated in the Ruhr basin are pumped over into the watershed of the Emscher.

The Emscher, which has been fully lined with concrete and converted into a single-purpose stream, is sometimes referred to as the *cloaca maxima* of the Ruhr area. The only quality objective is the avoidance of aesthetic nuisance, and this is achieved by mechanical (primary) treatment of effluents entering the stream and by the rather slow rate of biological degradation in the stream itself. Also, by the use of plantings, gentle curves of the canalized stream, attractive design of bridges, etc., care is taken to give the Emscher as pleasing an appearance as circumstances permit. Since the Emscher can be used only for effluent discharge, the area is dependent upon adjoining watersheds for water supply and water-based recreation opportunities. This presents little hardship since the distances are small, and the streams are parallel.

Near its mouth the entire flow of the Emscher up to about 1,000 cfs is treated mechanically to remove most of the suspended matter, thus

[5] See Ciriacy-Wantrup, *op. cit.*; and Allen V. and Georgia Kneese, "The Recent German Detergents Legislation: Nature and Rationale," Resources for the Future, Inc., mimeo., 1962.

[6] However, the quality of the Ruhr varies considerably along the course of its flow. At the head of the Hengsteysee (a shallow reservoir in the Ruhr built essentially as an instream treatment plant) the quality of the water is very poor. Neutralization, precipitation, and oxidation occur in the Hengsteysee, and further stabilization takes place in the Harkortsee, a similar instream oxidation lake, and by the time the water reaches the Baldeneysee (a third such lake) at Essen the quality has improved to such an extent that the water is suitable for general recreation use. This is true despite the fact that there are further heavy discharges of treated wastes between the Hengsteysee and the Baldeneysee. These waste discharges are generally given far-reaching treatment, frequently by means of treatment plants with double biological stages.

making possible the realization of scale economies in treatment to a far-reaching extent. The heavy burden put on the Rhine both from upstream sources and from the Ruhr industrial area (largely via the Emscher) has caused great downstream costs. This is especially true in Holland where even recently introduced large-scale groundwater recharge projects are failing to supply water of a suitable quality. Consequently, the Emschergenossenschaft is now laying detailed plans for biological treatment of the Emscher, which experiments indicate will be highly successful. For example, a test plant is achieving 98 per cent degradation of phenols, which are one of the most expensive and difficult substances to deal with in treating raw water supplies. When biological treatment of the entire Emscher flow is accomplished, the contribution of the Ruhr industrial area to Rhine River pollution will be substantially mitigated,[7] and the area will be essentially a closed water supply and waste water system.

While formal optimization procedures were not utilized by the *Genossenschaften*, they have probably realized their major gains from viewing the problem of waste disposal and water supply as one of integrated system design. They have made extensive use of scale economies in treatment by linking several towns and cities to a single plant in cases where the cost of transporting effluents to the plants was less than the additional scale economies that could be realized. In the case of the Emscher they have linked an entire watershed to a single treatment plant. They have combined industrial and household wastes when joint treatment seemed more efficient. They have made use of stream specialization for recreation and water supply purposes and of artificial groundwater recharge for quality improvement purposes. They have at various times and places used flow augmentation and direct aeration of streams. They have explicitly considered the differential ability of streams to degrade wastes at various locations both in determining location of treatment plants and in influencing the location of industrial plants. Where scale economies or special technical competence of their staff merited it, they have established their own waste recovery plants;

---

[7] Except for saline pollution from the coal mines in the area. The Lippe carries considerable natural salinity and additional saline water is pumped up from the mines. Another major source of salinity in the Rhine is the potash industry, particularly in France. Effective arrangements for reducing salinity have not yet been made.

in other instances, they have induced waste recovery or process changes by levying charges for effluent discharge based on quantity and quality of waste water and by acting as a co-operative marketing agency for recovered waste products. Decisions between alternative ways of achieving objectives have, at least in a rough and ready fashion, been based upon consideration of cost "tradeoffs" between them.[8] Finally, and of considerable importance, they have provided for monitoring of the streams, especially those used for water supply, and for operation of facilities to take account of changing conditions in a more or less continuous fashion.

Whether the use of the Emscher as an open sewer, or the very heavy use of waste degradation capacity on certain stretches of the Ruhr, is optimal cannot be conclusively determined partly because explicit valuations of recreation use have not been made.[9] Actually, however, outdoor recreation is quite impressively catered to in the Ruhr area, partly because of the considerable power which the communities and counties exercise in both the water *Genossenschaften* and the Siedlungsverband (the agency responsible for land use planning in the Ruhr area). Coordination between the work of the Siedlungsverband and the *Genossenschaften* has contributed to the explicit weighing of recreational and aesthetic values against others in the development and use of water resources, and to the explicit consideration of industrial location as a variable in water use and waste disposal planning.

[8] Administrators of the *Genossenschaften* place great emphasis on the economies which result from a single staff planning, building, operating, and supervising the water resources facilities of an entire basin. The Ruhrverband-Ruhrtalsperrenverein operates 84 effluent treatment plants (to which, on the average, 4 new ones are added each year), 4 large detention lakes, 27 pumpworks, 300 km. of trunk sewer, run-of-the-river power plants, 6 dams (one in addition is under construction), power plants associated with the dams, and their own electricity distribution systems. The total staff, including laborers, apprentices and janitorial help, is 780 persons. See H. W. Koenig, *op. cit.*, p. 157.

[9] Actually the Emscher was an out-of-control and extremely offensive open sewer when the Emschergenossenschaft came into existence. Dr. Knop, Executive Director of the Emschergenossenschaft, has commented on this issue as follows: "In the study of the Emscher it is well to note that the Emscher area has a concentration of population of 3400 per km², which is comparable to that of large German cities like Frankfurt and Cologne. At low water the discharge of the Emscher at its mouth consists of 90% waste water and only 10% natural flow. This corresponds also to the conditions found in most municipal sewers. It is unthinkable to divide treatment among countless points in this system in order to raise the quality of water in the Emscher to usable levels." Translated from a communication by Dr. Knop to the author.

THE COST-ASSESSMENT PROCEDURES

Before turning directly to the assessment of waste disposal costs, it may be of interest to cite a couple of examples of how charges are used in connection with Genossenschaft activities not directly concerned with waste disposal. The first indicates how offsite costs are caused to be reflected, at least in part, in decisions affecting land subsidence, and the second shows how special benefits to particular members can be reflected in the system design if the special beneficiaries bear the incremental costs.

The major subsidence problem in the Ruhr region is in the area of the Emschergenossenschaft. Indeed, this earliest of the *Genossenschaften* was established to deal with the highly interdependent problems of waste disposal and drainage in the Emscher watershed, which had been severely affected by subsidence before the turn of the century. At the present time about one third of the area of the Emschergenossenschaft is low-lying land without natural drainage. By far the greatest amount of capital and maintenance expenditures of that organization have been for land drainage purposes.

For the initial drainage work, costs were divided half and half between the mines and the immediate beneficiaries of the drainage. This reflected a calculation made at the time that about half of the expenditure on the initial system was not attributable to subsidence stemming from coal mining activity. The proportionate assessments upon the beneficiaries were computed on a detailed basis depending upon such variables as area, land value, elevation, etc. The initial drainage system was an expensive operation, involving the canalization of the main stem and establishment of numerous large pumping plants.

The mining industry pays for damages occasioned by later subsidence (including further loss of natural drainage and damage to canalized streams). This provides an incentive to plan co-operatively to maximize the net value of coal production, and at least those technological "spillovers" which affect waste disposal and drainage are considered in the development of the mines. One-fourth of the "spillover" costs are paid by the specific mine directly causing the damage, the remainder are borne by the industry as a whole. On incentive grounds, one might suppose that the mine directly responsible should bear the full cost. The method used is sometimes justified on the grounds that such sharing is consistent with the Genossenschaft principle, and sometimes by the statement that it is a satisfactory means of sharing the cost of uncertainty. In this case, the uncertainty results from the impossibility of fully forecasting costs that may result from future subsidence.[10] Forecasts of the degree and cost of subsidence if certain areas are mined must be made available to industry if steps are to be taken to avoid damages. However, despite the efforts of the Emschergenossenschaft to produce sound estimates, the forecasts sometimes prove incorrect, especially for small areas. Consequently, a mining company may incur unnecessary costs in its attempt to avoid damages.

The second example illustrates another facet of the mode of operation of the *Genossenschaften*. Sometimes a member requests special facilities that are not needed to achieve the stated Genossenschaft objective. His request is checked with the over-all land use plan, and if it is not inconsistent with the Genossenschaft's general objectives and is within its competency, the work will be done and the additional costs will be assessed to the member. For example, in the 1930's when plans were being made for construction of the Baldeneysee, one of the large oxidation lakes in the Ruhr, the City of Essen foresaw the vast recreation potential and requested that the lake be located in a different place and enlarged beyond the size which had been planned solely on the basis of its function as a water purifier. The request was granted, and the additional costs were paid by the city. It is now generally agreed that the recreation value of the lake far exceeds its value as a water purification device. Regattas are held on the lake; there is swimming and camping along the edges; several excursion boats ply its waters; there are numerous attractive restaurants overlooking it; and on fine days it is covered with foldboats and sailboats of all types. Another example of work performed for specific beneficiaries is the dikes along the Rhine. The costs of these works are assessed to the various beneficiaries in proportion to the benefits they receive.

Rather than attempt to set out the waste disposal cost assessment sys-

---

[10] An excellent exposition of the nature and rationale of the cost assessments procedure with respect to subsidence is found in *Fuenfzig Jahre der Emschergenossenschaft, op. cit.*

tems used by the *Genossenschaften* in full detail, emphasis will be put upon central concepts. First, the system used by the Emschergenossenschaft-Lippeverband is described, then the ways in which the Ruhrverband method differs are indicated.[11] In both cases, the general principles will be outlined without stating all the actual departures which occur in practice. Among such departures are the following types: instances where rules of thumb are considered adequate and not worth changing in view of the costs involved in administering the new procedures (the procedures described were instituted within the past five years), lags in the application of new methods, political power factors in the organization itself.

One such departure results from the fact that there are certain areas, especially in the Lippe basin, where interdependency between fiscally independent units is not considered sufficiently close to make the "system concept" elsewhere used fully applicable.

The term "system concept" as used in this context requires a word of explanation. It is interpreted to mean that a waste-discharging unit will be assessed on the basis of the quantity and quality of effluent discharged into the system regardless of whether a treatment plant or

[11] Major references are *Emschergenossenschaft-Auszug aus der Veranlagung fuer das Rechnungsjahr 1962* (Emschergenossenschaft—Summary of Assessment Procedures for the Fiscal Year 1962); *Lippeverband Auszug aus der Veranlagung fuer das Rechnungsjahr 1962* (Lippeverband—Summary of Assessment Procedures for the Fiscal Year 1962); E. Knop, "Die Schaedlichkeits-bewertung von Abwaessern" (Evaluating the Damaging Effects of Effluents), *Technisch-Wissenschaftliche Mitteilungen,* Heft 4, Juli, 1961, Vulkan Verlag, Essen; *Fuenfzig Jahre Emschergenossenschaft, op. cit.,* pp. 103, 123; *Veranlagung zum Ruhrverband,* Gueltig ab 1 Januar 1962 (Assessment of the Ruhrverband, effective as of January 1, 1962), Ruhrverband, Essen; *Veranlagung zum Ruhrtalsperrenverein,* Gueltig ab 1, Januar 1962. (Assessment of the Ruhrtalsperrenverein, effective as of January 1, 1962), Ruhrverband, Essen; W. Bucksteeg, *Verfahren zur Bestimmung des Einwohnergleichwerts beliebiger Abwaesser* (Procedure for Determination of the Population Equivalence of Varied Effluents), Ruhrverband, Essen (mimeo.); W. Bucksteeg, "Problematik der Bewertung giftiger Inhaltsstoffe im Abwasser und Moeglichkeiten zur Schaffung gesicherter Bewertungsgrundlagen" (Problems in the Evaluation of Toxic Substances in Effluents and the Possibility of Obtaining Secure Evaluation Standards), *Muenchner Beitraege zur Abwaesser-, Fischerei- und Flussbiologie,* Band 6 (Muenchen: Verlag von R. Oldenbourg, 1959). An explanation of the cost allocation method of the Wupperverband is found in *Wupperverband Beitragsliste 1961* (Wupperverband Contribution List 1961), Wuppertal, Maerz 1961, and for the Niersverband in *Niersverband Hebeliste fuer das Rechnungsjahr 1962* (Niersverband Assessment List for the Fiscal Year 1962), Niersverband, Viersen. Much of the following description is also based upon conversation with the staffs of the *Genossenschaften* and upon correspondence with Dr. Knop, Executive Director of the Emschergenossenschaft-Lippeverband, and with Dr. Koenig, Executive Director of the Ruhrverband-Ruhrtalsperrenverein.

other abatement measure is instituted specifically for that outfall. Costs are distributed among dischargers on the basis of a computation of the burden put upon the system, not on the basis of specific design features of the system. In this way, treatment can be carried quite far at points where scale economies make it relatively inexpensive, and it can be omitted or reduced at points where it is more expensive to achieve the same stream objectives. Moreover, it permits such measures as stream treatment plants, flow augmentation, and artificial reaeration of streams to be used in a way that will minimize total costs to the system, while meeting the stream standards which have been set.

Whenever a new plant in the jurisdictional area of the *Genossenschaften* chooses a location with respect to existing facilities or the assimilative capacity of the stream which entails extra costs, such costs may be laid upon the waste discharger. These costs might include the cost of a special treatment plant built to handle the new plant's waste or the cost of transporting its wastes to existing facilities.

Emschergenossenschaft-Lippeverband Effluent Charge Assessment Method

The method of determining effluent charges used by the Emschergenossenschaft endeavors to distribute the costs of the water quality management system in some reasonable proportion to the quantity and quality of the individual effluents which cause the costs to be incurred. No effort is here made to describe in full detail the laboratory tests upon which the method is based. Some understanding of the technical (chemical-biological) underpinnings is essential, however, if the economic merits and shortcomings of the method are to be understood. The basic principles of the Emschergenossenschaft-Lippeverband method are readily explained by the use of the following formula:

$$D = -1 + \frac{S}{S_p} + \frac{1}{2}\frac{B}{B_p} + \frac{1}{2}\frac{P-30}{P_p} + F$$

D = Dilution factor
S = Materials subject sedimentation in cm³/1
S_p = Permitted S in cm³/1
B = BOD$_5$ in mg/1 after sedimentation

B_p = Permitted BOD_5 in mg/1

P = Potassium permanganate oxygen used in mg/1 after sedimentation

P_p = Permitted potassium permanganate use in mg/1

F = Toxicity to fish as determined by dilution method

The characteristic which permits the various pollutants to be handled as commensurables in the formula is their damaging effect on fish. Indeed, the formula indicates the amount of clean water required to dilute the effluent in order to avoid harm to fish. On this basis, the degree of pollution (fish damage) caused by greatly differing types of polluting agents can be expressed as single, commensurable numbers. The effluent is tested before it is treated in the system treatment plant but after any pretreatment by the manufacturers. Communities do not provide any type of pretreatment.

In each term of the equation the numerator indicates the actual amount of a polluting substance found in the effluent sample, and the denominator indicates a permitted amount of the substance. The ratio, of course, represents a dilution factor. It is important to note that the individually derived dilution factors are held to be additive in character.[12] To this end, the water is aerated during the toxicity dilution test to prevent oxygen shortage from developing and influencing the result. The product of the aggregate dilution factor and the quantity of effluent as compared with all other similarly obtained products indicates the share of over-all costs which an individual effluent discharger is to pay. It must be noted that the indicated procedure is not regarded as fully ideal but as one which produces usable results while requiring a comparatively modest number of relatively simple chemical and biological tests. The described procedure, though something of an idealization of the procedures actually used, clearly illustrates the principle favored and largely applied by the Emschergenossenschaft-Lippeverband. Moreover, future Emschergenossenschaft cost allocations are to be based on it in an increasingly consistent fashion. The same points hold true for the Ruhrverband procedure described subsequently.

[12] The importance of this in simplifying any procedure which endeavors to distribute costs to individual waste dischargers will be apparent from the discussion in chapter 4.

A somewhat more detailed discussion of the reasons for the individual terms in the formula will aid in understanding its over-all rationale.[13]

The second term relates to materials in suspension which will settle out of the effluent. These substances may be either degradable (oxygen-consuming) organics or non-degradable material. Unless the non-degradable material is removed from the effluent, it can cause substantial biological damage by settling out and covering the bottom of the stream and killing organisms entering the food chain of fish. On this ground, the rule of thumb is adopted that substances subject to sedimentation, whether organic or inorganic, will require the same amount of dilution. The permitted quantity in $cm^3/1$ is one which is deemed to be just low enough not to harm fish life under the conditions of the area. For the organic materials (which provide the standard for the inorganics) permissible quantity is determined on the basis of oxygen demand (see below).

The next two terms relate to degradable organic substances which are in solution. This is roughly the degradable material which would be left in the effluent after so-called "primary" (or as it is termed in Germany "mechanical") treatment without the addition of chemical precipitating agents, i.e., 60–75 per cent of the degradable material in household waste.[14] It will be noted that each of these terms is given one-half weight. This reflects the fact that of the two methods for testing the BOD (biochemical oxygen demand) of degradable organic wastes, both are biased when the stream and the effluent contain varying amounts of toxic material. The BOD_5 test establishes the amount of oxygen consumed by bacteria in a sample of effluent incubated over a period of five days under controlled temperature and light conditions.[15] The difficulty with the BOD_5 test which led the Emschergenossenschaft-Lippeverband to include the potassium perman-

---

[13] The following discussion is based upon the article by E. Knop, "Die Schaedlichkeitsbewertung von Abwaessern," *op. cit.;* and upon discussion with Dr. Knop and members of his staff, particularly, Drs. Husman, Philipsen, and Sons.

[14] Karl Imhoff, *Taschenbuch der Stadtentwaesserung* (Handbook of Municipal Drainage) (Muenchen: Verlag von R. Oldenbourg, 1962).

[15] See Gordon Maskew Fair and John Charles Geyer, *Water Supply and Waste-Water Disposal* (New York: John Wiley and Sons, 1956), pp. 542-43, for an explanation of the exact procedures by which this test is carried through.

ganate test in the allocation formula is that when toxic substances are present in the effluent, bacteriological action may be slowed down and the test will yield too low a BOD value. When such an effluent is put into a receiving water which contains less toxic material than the effluent sample, biological activity is more intense than in the sample and the predicted rate of BOD exertion is too low. Consequently, the dissolved oxygen in the stream is called upon to a greater degree than forecasts based upon the laboratory test would have indicated.

The potassium permanganate test, on the other hand, is based upon chemical oxidation of materials in the effluent. The potassium permanganate oxidizes some (inorganic) materials which would not be degraded by bacteria in a stream, even under ideal conditions for biological action. Thus this test is not a direct indication of the decomposability of the organic matter in the effluent, but it yields an estimate of total oxidizable material including some inorganic material and some organic material which does not oxidize in the stream. Since it is based upon *chemical* oxidation, the result it yields is not influenced by the presence of toxic materials.[16]

The equation indicates that 30 is to be subtracted from P in the numerator of the fourth term. This is an estimate of the amount of *non-biologically* degradable material registered by the permanganate test. It will be noticed that the third and fourth terms are each given one-half weight in the equation. This results from the fact that the combined effect of the two tests (with the result of the potassium permanganate test adjusted as indicated) is held to provide an approximation of the degradability of organic wastes in a receiving water containing some toxic materials. The permissible amount of oxygen demand (the donominators of the third and fourth terms) is set at a level that is calculated to prevent dissolved oxygen from falling below the

[16] The way in which chemical oxygen demand is measured varies considerably from country to country. COD tests apparently are rarely performed in the United States (perhaps because of the lesser amounts of toxic substances found in American effluents in past years), but when such tests are performed there is a preference for potassium dichromate (see Fair and Geyer, *op. cit.*, p. 542). In England potassium permanganate is typically used and a sample effluent oxidized for four hours at 27°C; see Louis Klein, *op. cit.*, p. 379. In Germany the sample is boiled for 10 minutes and yields a value four times as high as the English method. See Karl Imhoff, *op. cit.*, p. 95.

3 to 4 mg/1 which is necessary to sustain the types of fish life found in the area.[17]

The fifth term in the formula indicates the necessary dilution for toxic materials and its value is derived directly from a fish toxicity test. During the test period the effluent is constantly aerated in order to compensate for the action of the oxygen-consuming waste. The period of the test is 48 hours, and the dilution standard is determined on the basis of absence of noticeable damage to the fish during the test period.

The initial term (-1) compensates for the fact that the discharge of waste products includes a volume of dilution water.

Several additional calculations are made in finally establishing the share of costs to be attributed to a specific polluter. Two of these relate to strength and heat of the effluent: (1) It is considered that the costs of dealing with wastes do not rise in one-to-one correspondence with the strength of the effluent, and stronger wastes are assessed at a proportionately lower rate than more dilute wastes; (2) for hot effluents, an additional cost is assessed to cover the extra dilution that is required because heat not only stimulates BOD but reduces the oxygen saturation level of the receiving water.

Ruhrverband Cost Assessment

The Emschergenossenschaft system of cost assessment achieves commensurability between varied effluents by determining their propensity to kill a given type of test fish. This permits all effluents to be evaluated in terms of a single numerical scale. The choice of the objective of maintaining fish life does not necessarily mean the absence of other objectives; it is simply considered a useful summary surrogate for a wide range of values. Thus it may well be held that such other objectives as aesthetics and public health are adequately met if the fish objective is met.

The Ruhrverband also achieves commensurability between various types of waste materials by basing its procedure on a single physical

[17] The actual p values used in the equation are as follows:

$$D = -1 + \frac{S}{0.4} + \frac{1}{2}\frac{B}{40} + \frac{1}{2}\frac{P - 30}{42} + F$$

objective, but a somewhat different one.[18] The objective implied by the Ruhrverband's technique is that the self-purification capacity of the stream (and the organic waste degradation capacity of biological treatment plants) is to be maximized. With this objective in view, a method was developed which is capable of integrating into a single measure the effects of organic wastes and of toxic waste. The measure used is a special form of the population equivalent BOD.

Population equivalent BOD is a common measure of organic waste load both in the United States and in Europe. One population equivalent is the oxygen demand which, on the average, the untreated daily wastes of one human being would exert over a specified time period (usually five days). Population equivalent BOD has long been a method of stating the organic pollution loads generated by industry. In general, it is a very undependable measure of industrial waste loads since it does not comprehend the destructive effects of substances other than oxygen-demanding organic materials found in industrial wastes. The Ruhrverband has, however, developed a population equivalent measure which aims to include both oxygen-demanding and toxic wastes. The character of this measure, and its rationale, has been stated as follows:

> . . . it was possible, in the course of recent years, to develop a test which makes it possible to judge every effluent, regardless of its composition, by its population equivalent. In doing this we start with the presumption that household (and other oxygen-demanding) wastes, as well as toxic wastes, work themselves out in a very similar fashion even though through different mechanisms. The self-purification of a stream over a given stretch is similarly affected by both types of effluents, in the one case due to additional pollution, in the other through inhibition of the self-purification process. The opportunity thus presents itself to form an equivalence between these two effects and to assign a population equivalent value of 3 to the quantity of industrial effluent which has the same inhibiting effect

[18] The following discussion is largely based upon W. Bucksteeg, "Teste zur Beurteilung von Abwaessern" (Tests for the Judgment of Effluents), *Staedtehygiene,* 9, 1961, and "Problematik der Bewertung giftiger Inhaltsstoffe im Abwasser und Moeglichkeiten zur Schaffung gesicherter Bewertungsgrundlagen" (Problems in the Evaluation of Toxic Substances in Effluents and the Possibility of Obtaining Secure Evaluation Standards), *op. cit.,* and conversation with Drs. Bucksteeg and Thiele of the Ruhrverband laboratories.

on self-purification as a household effluent of, for example, 162 g (54 g BOD = 1 population equivalent) with a population equivalent of 3. Clearly this method is contestable at many points; still it seemed to us a usable point of departure, and we have developed an easily executed test on this basis which has already yielded numerous good results . . . about the test itself I would just like to say that we use two rows of Erlenmeyer flasks which contain a standard solution [standard solution of an organic substance of known degradability] and a small amount of activated sludge. To one row are added increasing amounts of household effluent of

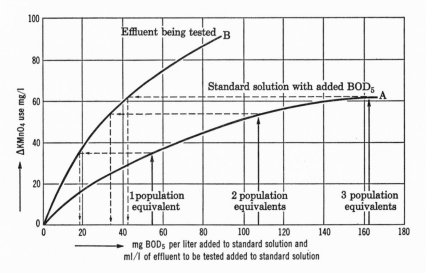

Figure 18. Determination of the population equivalent of industrial effluents.

which the BOD_5 is simultaneously determined, and to the other increasing amounts of the effluent to be tested. The flasks are then shaken for three days on a shaking device and after this time the potassium permanganate demand of the filtered contents of the bottles is determined.

If the differences between the $KMnO_4$ use of the individual concentrations (the concentration of the known household effluent measured in additions of mg $BOD_5/1$ and the test effluent in additions of ml/1) are carried into a co-ordinate system, we obtain the type of curves indicated in the illustration [see Figure 18]. These curves are used in the following way: we find the points for 54, 108, and 162 BOD (1, 2, and 3 population equivalents, respectively) on the A-curve, carry them to the B-curve and from there read to the abscissa. In the illustrated case the corresponding values are 18, 34, and 42 mg/l. Accordingly, $\frac{94}{6} = 15.7$ liters of the test effluent are to be valued at one population equivalent. The main advantage of this procedure is that all factors influencing self-purification including oxygen demanding and toxic qualities are comprehended simultaneously.[19]

An additional merit of the described test is, according to Dr. Bucksteeg, that biological degradation processes are unusually sensitive to toxins, more sensitive than fish, for example.

As indicated earlier, both the Emschergenossenschaft and the Ruhrverband are able to measure the "pollution effect" of varied wastes along a single scale because their procedures are contingent upon the effects of varied effluents upon a single physical phenomenon. As will be indicated subsequently, the principle underlying the cost allocation technique is not precisely consistent with the objective of the pollution abatement activities of the *Genossenschaften*.

COMMENT ON THE COST-ASSESSMENT PROCEDURES

The cost-assessment procedures used by the *Genossenschaften* depart in some ways from the economic principles discussed earlier in this study. The minimization of costs either in the limited sense of minimizing costs for given objectives, or in the broader sense of minimizing the social costs associated with waste disposal, logically implies that both the system design criteria and the cost assessment and distribution criteria must be based on costs and not directly upon physical effects. A decision between alternative methods cannot be logically made on the basis of physical performance and physical damages. It is *costs of alternatives foregone* that must be balanced at the margin.

[19] Translated from W. Bucksteeg, "Teste zur Beurteilung von Abwaessern" (Tests for the Judgment of Effluents), *op. cit.*, p. 4. A detailed set of laboratory instructions is found in W. Bucksteeg, "Verfahren zur Bestimmung des Einwohnergleichwertes beliebiger Abwaesser," *op. cit.* In practice, the charge levied upon individual polluters is made contingent upon some simple indicator of production or waste discharge with adjustments made when the quality and/or quantity of waste discharge changes.

Similarly, in principle, a cost assessment method that is based on physical results alone will not distribute costs properly and consequently will not provide the appropriate incentives for the reduction of waste loads.

It must be recognized, however, that certain costs of implementation that are ordinarily and properly neglected in reasoning about the character of ideal procedures cannot be neglected in practice. Methods that are less than theoretically ideal may be optimal in practice, since an important element in determining the best method for actual use is the cost of making marginal refinements. A comparatively crude method that is correct in principle will often realize the major share of the gains which could be achieved by more complex and conceptually more satisfying techniques.

The value of simplicity is stressed again and again by the officials of the *Genossenschaften,* and most of the admittedly arbitrary elements in their procedures result from a specific judgment that further refinement is not justifiable. For example, the acute fish toxicity test used by the Emschergenossenschaft is only a crude approximation of the actual effect of toxins on fish populations, and it is recognized as such. It is well known that toxins affect fish differently in different life stages, that they may hinder reproduction, and that some of the most important effects may come through the food chain.[20] Each year sees many studies of the sometimes complex and indirect effects of toxins on the ecology of waste-receiving waters.[21] In the absence of a full identification of all possible effects of all possible combinations of toxins of effluent origin, a fully satisfactory procedure is out of the question. In the present state of knowledge some sort of acute toxicity test (possibly with safety margins based on some form of benchmark studies) may well be the best practical procedure for quickly estimating the toxicity of a substance to fish.

Simplification extends to other aspects of cost assessment. Both the Emschergenossenschaft and Ruhrverband procedures give only

[20] See for example the papers in U.S. Department of Health, Education and Welfare, *Biological Problems in Water Pollution, Transactions of the 1959 Seminar,* The Robert A. Taft Sanitary Engineering Center, Technical Report WGO-3, Cincinnati, 1960.

[21] See the annual literature reviews in the *Journal of the Water Pollution Control Federation.*

indirect recognition to the waste degradation and recovery processes which occur in the stream.[22] The discharge of settled organic sewage into a stretch of stream where the oxygen resource is not depleted may cause little or no further damage in the stream, while even highly treated sewage (which always has some residual oxygen demand) may cause difficulties if discharged into a critical zone. A hot effluent may have an even more striking differential effect. In a critical zone, it may kill fish or cause anaerobic conditions to develop; in a zone where the dissolved oxygen content is high, it may substitute for treatment or other measures by speeding the degradation process.

These considerations have by no means gone completely unnoticed in the *system* planning of the *Genossenschaften,* and *Abwasserlast-plaene* (effluent burden plans which identify areas where the stream is particularly heavily loaded) have in considerable measure determined the sites of treatment plants and the sequence of construction of plants. Similar considerations, however, have received only indirect attention in the assessment and assignment of costs. When new industrial or residential locations are planned, the *Genossenschaften* are consulted by the *Siedlungsverband,* the land planning authority.[23] In framing its recommendation to the land planning authority, the Genossenschaft studies the problem of waste disposal associated with the new plant or community, giving consideration to such factors as accessibility to existing treatment facilities, possible scale economies in the construction of new treatment facilities, and the ability of the stream to assimilate wastes. If the location recommendations of the *Genossenschaften* are not accepted, the additional costs to the system of an unfavorable location may be assessed to the industrial plant or the community.[24] In this way, the differential assimilative capacity

[22] These processes are described in chapter 2.

[23] This was the first planning authority to deal with the problems of land use planning in industrialized regions. For a description of the land use planning activities in the Ruhr industrial area see *Raumordnung, Raumforschung, Landes-planungsgesetzgebung in Nordrhein-Westfalen* (Land Use, Land Research, and Land Planning Legislation in Northrhine-Westphalia) (Duesseldorf: Droste Verlag, 1951); see also S. Kegel, *Der Siedlungsverband Ruhrkohlenbezirk* (The Land Development Association of the Ruhr Coal Area) (Duesseldorf: Droste Verlag, no publication date).

[24] Based on a conversation with Dr.-Ing. Rincke (Alternate Manager) of the Ruhrverband.

of streams can be indirectly recognized in the cost assessment formulas through side calculations.

From an economic point of view, charges must be varied to reflect costs if they are to be optimal. Unless charges are increased in stretches of a stream where the costs of damages and abatement services are highest, they will not provide the appropriate incentive to waste dischargers to reduce waste discharge and avoid location in these areas. Problems of system design operation and appropriate cost distribution, which can really be viewed as parts of the same problem, may be eased by recent methodological developments in Germany and in the United States. These hold promise for more accurate consideration of stream assimilative capacity and aim at techniques for rapid determination of the condition of a stream at specific points.[25] They will help to determine the character of a stream with and without particular discharges, or with various levels of discharge stemming from a particular waste discharger.[26,27]

[25] See R. L. O'Connell, J. B. Cohen, E. C. Tsivoglou, "Future Stream Flow Requirements for Organic Pollution Abatement Ohio River Basin" (mimeo.), U.S. Public Health Service, Robert A. Taft Sanitary Engineering Center, to be published. A procedure of the general type outlined in the above study is to be applied to the Illinois River also. H. W. Poston, "The Great Lakes and Illinois River Basin Project" (mimeo.) prepared for presentation at the semi-annual meeting of the Great Lakes Commission, at Mackinac Island, Michigan, on July 23–24, 1962, p. 5. Dr. Boehnke, Bauassesor, Emschergenossenschaft, "Abwasserlastplaene fuer Industriefluesse" (Effluent Burden Plans for Industrial Rivers) to be published. Experiments testing the applicability of such models have also been carried through by the Battelle-Institut, Frankfurt/Main, Germany, under the sponsorship of the Ministry of Atomic Energy and Water Economics (whose water resources responsibilities have now been turned over to the Ministry of Public Health). See "Kurzberichte der Wasserwirtschaft" (Short Notices about Water Economics), *Die Wasserwirtschaft*, February, 1962, p. 56. None of the models thus far developed comprehends the plant nutrient, algae growth, and decay sequence which can be expected to grow in importance as streams become more heavily loaded, since even advanced orthodox treatment removes plant nutrients from the effluent to only a minor degree. Also longer delayed "second stage" effects on oxygen balance due to nitrification are not included. Comprehension of these effects into predictive models will require considerably more secure knowledge of chemical, physical, and biological relationships than is presently available.

[26] Dr. Knop, of the Emschergenossenschaft, has commented as follows on the foregoing sections.

"It would not be suitable or necessary to distinguish between the locations of the outfalls. This is immediately apparent in regard to the Emscher because here the self-purification powers play no role and abatement activity is based on the demands of quality in the Rhine. But the Rhine is also a natural extension of the

Although the *Genossenschaften* make side calculations which take some account of the fact that rigid application of the cost allocation procedure can result in assessments that are not appropriate, the cost assessment procedure is not fully consistent with the design procedure. As previously stated, this is the limited one of approximately minimizing the costs associated with waste disposal given certain stated standards of stream quality. To be consistent with this objective, each discharger should bear the system costs for which he is responsible.

In order to arrive at a formula for allocating costs that will induce appropriate waste-reducing decisions, appropriate cost weights would have to be applied to a measure of volume of polluting substance. Ideally these weights would represent the incremental costs of a given discharge into the system. In the case of an organization that directly provides most treatment services this should include the incremental cost of treatment, damages, and flow regulation optimally balanced. When certain stream standards are to be met (in contrast to a full-scale optimization), the incremental costs of the facilities provided by the central agency for meeting them are the relevant ones. The latter more realistically describes the situation of the *Genossenschaften*.

The *Genossenschaften* assessment system makes no provision for systematically taking into account variations in incremental costs resulting from variable streamflow. If the costs of waste discharge to the discharger do not vary in accordance with flow, there is no incentive

Lippe and the Ruhr. The handling of waste waters must also, in this case, consider the demands of the Rhine. In addition, the Ruhr is used precisely in its lower stretches as a source of drinking water. One could in this regard even argue that the outfalls on the upper part of the stream are not as damaging as those on the lower reaches since, because of the self-purification powers of the stream, a portion of the damaging pollution load is degraded. In sum it seems to me that it is not sensible or feasible to distinguish between outfalls because of the comparatively small extent of the areas of the Genossenschaften. In this regard, there are vast differences between the areas of the West German Genossenschaften and the gigantic river basins in the United States." (Translated from a communication to the author.)

[27] In the case of non-degradable pollutants the problem of tracing physical concentrations is much less difficult than with degradable substances since essentially only dilution is involved. However, the cost of disposing of substances creating conditions of hardness, acidity, alkalinity, salinity, etc., in water, into water courses is a function of the number and value of reuses. Again, this means that the location of discharge is not a matter of indifference.

to reduce discharges during low flow periods, even though the concentration of pollutants and attendant damages tend to rise sharply during low stream stages.

In assessing the merits of applying peak load pricing principles to effluent discharges the costs of determining variation in the quality and quantity of effluent over the relevant period must of course be considered. The costs of operating a sampling program along present lines would mount sharply if an effort were made to determine quality and quantity variation with sufficient continuity to permit peak load pricing.[28]

As previously indicated, in recent years progress has been made in the development of automatic monitoring devices. Such variables of river quality as dissolved oxygen, acidity-alkalinity, salinity, specific conductance (dissolved solids), temperature, and turbidity can be continuously measured with fairly simple devices. These devices appear to hold considerable promise as a tool for economically appropriate assessment of charges.

In general, the methods adopted by the *Genossenschaften* do not assess the specific incremental costs of particular discharges. However, they constitute a more or less reasonable way of distributing the long-run and current operating costs of the physical features of the system without systematic regard to location or timing of discharge.

It should be pointed out once more that from the point of view of resource allocation the method of charging adopted—or indeed whether effluent charges are made at all—would be relatively unimportant if waste loads delivered to the system were unresponsive to the charges imposed on them. However, through product and process adjustments, through waste recovery, through separation of wastes and various forms of pretreatment, industrial waste loads can be altered over very wide ranges.[29] Bucksteeg has reported on some of the existing differences in the BOD of industries with organic waste

---

[28] The Ruhrverband has 718 directly assessed industrial members and 264 communities. There would seem to be little to be accomplished by attempting to estimate changes in effluent quantity and quality from the communities themselves, since they appear to have little opportunity to adapt discharges to variable streamflow quantity and quality.

[29] W. Bucksteeg, "Problematik der Bewertung giftiger Inhaltsstoffe . . . ," *op. cit.*, p. 12, and "Teste zur Beurteilung von Abwaessern," *op. cit.*, p. 1.

loads. His own study of 14 paper mills indicated a population equivalent BOD per ton of paper ranging from 51 to 1,254, a multiple of almost 25. He also reported ranges per ton of output for other industries, in part based on the work of others. Multiples computed from the ranges reported in these industries are 2.5 in malt factories, 6 in starch factories, 4 and 50 respectively for beef and pork slaughter houses, about 10 in tanneries and about 20 in textile factories. As might be expected in the presence of such a range of possibilities, waste loads delivered to the *Genossenschaften's* quality control system have responded to effluent charges and other measures used to diminish them.

In general, the associations consider indirect methods of reducing wastes, such as recovery and process changes, as on a par with treatment. The phenol recovery plants operated by the Emschergenossenschaft, which recover about 65 per cent of the waste phenols in the basin,[30] are virtually self-sufficient. It seems likely that a comparable job could have been done through private action, for even a modest effluent charge could have caused individual firms to operate such plants. However, economies of marketing, staff, and research are thought to have been achieved by centralized operation.

Salvage of iron sulfate and sulfuric acid from the waste water of the Ruhr's iron and steel industry is another example of intensive waste recovery. Of the total amount of industrial acid used in the Ruhr area, over 30 per cent is recovered. Recovery even though usually carried on at a loss is often considerably cheaper than treatment by neutralization.[31] The incentive is a combination of effluent charges and technical marketing assistance offered by the Ruhrverband. In one steel plant at Dortmund a series of treatment and recirculation processes virtually eliminates effluent from the plant. This is attributed to a combination of water costs and effluent charges.[32] Other iron and steel

[30] *Fuenfzig Jahre Emschergenossenschaft, op. cit.,* p. 256.

[31] W. Husman, "Die Abwaesser der metallverarbeitenden Industrien" (The Effluents of the Metal Working Industries), *Beseitigung und Reinigung industrieller Abwasser,* Basel, 1958, p. 8.

[32] Based on a conversation with Mr. Maximilian Zur who is in charge of water management at the Hoesch-Westfalenhuette. See also Maximilian Zur, "Die Wasserwirtschaft der Hoesch-Westfalenhuette A.G., Dortmund" (The Water Management of the Hoesch-Westfalenhuette, Inc., Dortmund), *Stahl und Eisen,* Heft 17, 1958. Among the more interesting of the water saving procedures incorporated in the Westfalenhuette is the use of high-pressure boiler feed water in several of the

plants in the area are gradually adopting similar measures to reduce their water use and waste water generation.

CONCLUDING COMMENTS

The foregoing critique of the procedures used by the *Genossenschaften* contains no information about the administrative costs of achieving a more precise and theoretically correct system of cost assessment. This being the case, it cannot be conclusively established that the systems presently in use are inferior to more refined procedures. Where the primary objective of abatement works is protection of the Rhine and there is relatively little degradation of wastes, as is the case with the Emscher, efforts at discriminating on the basis of location may be of minor value. Also, where there is little variation in flow, as in the Emscher, peak load pricing would be of limited utility. Moreover, peak load pricing would no doubt require substantially higher expenditures for monitoring.

Because of considerations of this kind the above critique should be considered not so much as a demonstration that the procedures in the Ruhr area should be changed but as a reiteration of the fact that the assessment of costs is really *an important part* of system design and should be considered with the same care as other elements of the system. It is an important device for inducing efficient behavior in the absence of full centralization of decisions and its potentials in that regard should be fully identified and evaluated.

Furthermore, questions raised about specific features of the Genossenschaft procedures should not be permitted to obscure the achievements of these organizations. The design and operation of a regional system of waste disposal and water supply management taking extensive advantage of economies realizable through integrated design, explicitly taking into account efficiencies achievable through the reflections of regional waste disposal costs in industrial location and process design decisions, and incorporating cost assessment systems based upon concepts of pollution damages and independent of specific

---

cooling systems—including blast furnace cooling. The water is evaporated in the cooling process, the steam is heated further, and is then fed into the high pressure steam system. In this way not only water but also heat is conserved in the plant.

system elements is a pioneering achievement of the first order. The works of these organizations merits the closest attention of all those concerned with the difficult set of problems presented by water resources management in basins containing urban industrial complexes.

Part IV

Implementation and Administration

8

Establishing a Water Quality Management System

〜〜〜〜〜〜〜〜〜〜〜〜〜〜〜〜〜〜〜〜〜〜〜〜〜〜〜〜〜〜

It is the thesis of this study that more systematic approaches to water quality management can be developed and that in view of the rapidly growing burden of costs associated with waste disposal such approaches are urgently needed. Failure to provide them may result in some cases in unwarranted investments for waste disposal and in others in a deterioration of water quality which imposes unwarranted costs upon actual and prospective water users. Problems as intense as those that faced the Ruhr fifty years ago are appearing in parts of the United States today.

Many of the difficulties are institutional ones that become apparent when an attempt is made to establish measures for more systematic and rational water quality management. Questions arise about the size of the area to be managed, the kind of an authority that should manage it, the structure of relationships between water authorities, private firms, and public agencies, including a proper allocation of costs and benefits.

Any water quality management system that attempts a reasonably precise balancing of the incremental costs—onsite, offsite, public, private—must meet several criteria. It must provide some incentives or direct control measures so that the firm or city responsible for disposing of wastes will reduce its waste to an appropriate extent through treatment, process adjustments, residual materials recovery, or temporary detention of wastes. The system must be able to take advantage of economies that can be achieved by measures going beyond those

191

that can be carried out efficiently at individual points of waste outfall and water use. These may occur, for example, in waste treatment facilities, waste dilution, and stream specialization. The system must also provide some means of taking into account the difficult-to-measure values such as public health, aesthetic considerations, and recreational use of water resources because these are prominent considerations in water quality management.

If the system is to internalize major external costs and be capable of realizing regional economies in control measures, it must extend over a geographic area in which external costs from waste disposal are significant and in which there may be significant alternative opportunities for influencing water quality by large-scale measures. The area may be an entire river basin, a tributary basin, or a major portion of one of these. If stream specialization is important, the appropriate geographic area may constitute more than one hydrologic unit. But in any case, the area will follow watershed lines and in many instances will cross existing political ones. The appropriate definition of the planning and operating area is itself a major and difficult problem of system design.

ALTERNATIVE OPTIMIZATION SYSTEMS

Before a more detailed discussion of the problems of institutional arrangements, attention is given to the methods that can be used to achieve the desired levels of waste reduction at points of discharge and to co-ordinate individual alternatives and those provided by the central agency. Direct regulation, payments, and charges are the terms used here to refer to the techniques for achieving the system objective, which is to maximize the net benefits available from the water resource, or more specifically to minimize the costs associated with an optimum level of waste disposal. The alternatives are outlined in general terms, and no attempt is made to repeat many of the qualifications, technical complexities and data requirements dealt with in earlier chapters. Payments and charges, which were grouped in the analysis in chapters 4 and 5 because they are theoretically closely related, are treated separately here because they are very different in terms of administrative and institutional considerations.

Direct Regulation

This system would rely primarily upon direct public regulation of waste discharges in accordance with laws and administrative orders with respect to discharge at individual (industrial and municipal) outfalls. Such a system would constitute an extension or elaboration of existing policies and practices.

To be capable of optimizing under the regulatory system, the operating agency should be able to estimate not only the external costs associated with waste discharge but also the costs associated with incremental reductions in waste discharge by cities and firms through alternative means. It should be capable of taking into account possibilities for residual materials recovery, process changes, large-scale facilities, as well as conventional treatment.

Upon analysis of the physical and economic data bearing upon external costs and alternative means of reducing such costs, the agency would decide upon the combination of measures that would provide optimum results. Where economies exist in abatement measures that cannot be efficiently realized by the individual firm or city, it would provide such facilities. For all remaining waste discharges it would prescribe and enforce effluent standards that would optimize benefits from the water resource. Ideally, these standards would vary with streamflow conditions, and different standards would apply to different locations. Such variations would be necessary to take into account the differing waste-assimilation capacity of the watercourse under varying flow conditions, the differing capacity at various locations, and differing levels of demand upon the watercourse. The effluent standards would not only control the amount of existing discharges but, since they would vary geographically, play a role in determining the location of industrial and municipal outfalls. Optimum effluent standards might result in greatly different levels of required waste reduction at different outfalls, perhaps even at outfalls located close together.

The success of a system of this kind would depend in large measure upon the ability of an agency to develop reliable data on the physical and economic effects of alternative waste disposal programs and then to enforce effluent standards which minimize waste disposal costs to society. The funds for establishing and operating the system envisaged would presumably come from taxation, since neither the beneficiaries nor those responsible for the costs would be required to pay. This in itself presents a serious problem, since most taxes are not without distorting effects upon the allocation of resources.

Payments

This system would rely primarily on selective payments to waste contributors to motivate them to restrict waste discharge to an optimum degree. In other words, a payment would be made for each unit of waste withheld. This arrangement would constitute a departure from existing policy and practice and would entail a major change in the kinds of subsidies already provided.

On the basis of its estimate of the external costs, the operating agency would institute a schedule of payments for waste discharge reduction to induce cities and firms to reduce their waste contribution to an optimum level. These payments should in principle be equivalent to the downstream costs imposed by increments of waste discharge. Such payments would be intended to reduce the downstream costs associated with waste discharges to an optimum level. Payments would vary with streamflow conditions and with outfall locations, as well as with the quantity and quality of the effluent. Where the incremental costs associated with waste disposal can be reduced more efficiently by large-scale facilities than by payments, the agency would provide such facilities and reduce payments to reflect the efficiency gain.

No doubt some minimum direct regulatory measures would also be useful. For example, where a waterway is used for domestic water supplies and also has recreational and aesthetic values, it might be best simply to prohibit the discharge of virulently toxic chemicals and/or particularly unsightly and odorous materials.

This system would depend upon the agency expending relatively much larger sums, presumably raised through taxes, than the system utilizing effluent standards. The administering agency would need to have considerable discretion to make payments in accord with its estimates of the downstream consequences of increments of waste discharge.

Charges

This system would rely heavily upon effluent charges to motivate firms and cities to cut back on discharge in such a way as to optimize waste discharge. The elements of such a system would be identical with the payments system except that instead of making payments to waste contributors to reduce effluent discharges to optimum levels or setting standards to achieve the same purpose, charges would be levied on each unit of waste discharged. The schedule of charges would be based upon the external costs associated with increments of effluent discharge and therefore would vary with streamflow conditions and outfall locations. As with the system of payments, large-scale measures would be undertaken to the extent that their incremental costs are lower than the sum of the incremental individual outfall waste reduction costs and residual damages avoided by the measures.

Advantages and Disadvantages

These three alternative systems are representative of the range of possibilities that must be considered if greater efficiency in waste disposal is to be achieved. Each has certain advantages and disadvantages. The regulatory system in some ways constitutes the least departure from existing policy and practice. It would appear that direct regulation may be reasonably effective in dealing with the grossest forms of pollution but that it may be difficult to use for balancing incremental costs in a relatively precise manner. Moreover, it provides no funds for the construction and operation of measures of regional scope, should these prove economical.

The payment and charge systems are in effect an application of the pricing system—on which our economic institutions rely so heavily to secure an appropriate allocation of resources—to the waste disposal field. Under certain conditions which would appear to correspond to a range of important cases, neither the payment nor the charge system requires specific data on costs of reducing effluent discharges by various increments at individual outfalls. Some knowledge of the responsiveness of waste loads to the charges or payments in the region is, however, necessary for the planning of large-scale facilities.

These approaches place emphasis upon measuring external costs, and the individual payments and charges would be geared to this measurement. Both systems if ideally applied would provide an incentive to reduce effluent discharges to an optimal extent.

The payment system suffers from several major handicaps. The concept of paying a waste discharger for mitigation of the costs he imposes upon others is contrary to the view most people hold about what is an equitable practice—even if such a practice would assure greater economic efficiency. Even if this hurdle were overcome, the task would remain of raising the funds required—which would be quite substantial—through increased taxation. With so many urgent demands being placed upon government and the difficulty of framing taxes which themselves do not distort resources use, there are serious problems in securing the amounts required. Also, to be fully effective, payments must continue even after research produces lower cost means of reducing effluent or if the level of payments makes it profitable for a firm to cease manufacturing altogether in order to reduce its effluent contribution to the extent warranted by the payments. Even more problematical is the matter of firms which would locate in a basin except for the social cost of waste disposal which they would impose and which, therefore, would require payment even though they never locate in the basin. These amount to almost insuperable administrative obstacles to a fully effective system of subsidies.

The charges system does not suffer from these handicaps, but it may be opposed by the large waste contributors who now avoid the external costs which they impose. Moreover, the charges system would have the merit of providing funds to finance the construction and operation of quality management measures on a regional scale. If optimally applied, the charges system might yield somewhat more or less than the amount required for these purposes.

Actually the alternatives thus far outlined have not included all the activities which might be undertaken in a particularly far-reaching regional approach. For example, a regional agency might itself construct and operate treatment plants at individual outfalls as well as collective treatment plants, reservoirs for flow regulation, facilities for artificial reaeration of streams, etc. The *Genossenschaften* in the Ruhr area of Germany do all these things. The justification for the building of virtually all treatment plants (except those giving pre-treatment or special handling to industrial wastes) is largely in terms of economies of operation. First, precisely co-ordinated operation of plants is possible. Second, a small cadre of engineers can provide expert oversight of the operation of plants. Third, any innovation at one plant can be expeditiously applied to others where it may be merited. In other words, there may be economies of scale to be realized through co-ordinated development and operation of individual waste treatment facilities. Any regional agency for water quality management should certainly investigate the possibility of realizing such economies. However, an agency which undertakes such a breadth of program may use the best planning methods and adhere to correct principles of optimization and still fall short of arriving at an optimum system if it fails to devise means for efficiently combining these procedures with appropriate influence on decisions concerning industrial location, process design, water renovation and reuse, materials recovery, etc. The *Genossenschaften,* at least in a rough and ready way, achieve such co-ordination through a system of effluent charges, which also finances the costs of the quality management program.

PROBLEMS OF IMPLEMENTATION

It is evident that whatever system is selected to achieve more precise balancing of costs and returns with regard to waste disposal, some difficult practical problems must be overcome. The nature of these problems is briefly summarized in paragraphs which follow.

Physical and Economic Data Requirements

The measurement of external costs at a variety of locations under different streamflow conditions for increments of waste discharge is essential for any optimizing procedure. Yet, our knowledge of these matters is still so deficient that reasonably precise estimates of the *physical effects* can often not be provided on which to base cost estimates. Research designed to improve our knowledge in the entire area of damage costs is urgently needed. Should it be decided to rely primarily upon direct regulatory techniques, a large amount of data on the cost of incrementally reducing waste discharges would also be needed. At least some approximate data of this type would also be needed for all systems incorporating regional scale measures, regardless of the system of co-ordinating waste discharges. Such data would also be needed in instances where the cost of achieving a standard must be calculated. Only very limited data of this nature are now available. An earlier RFF study outlined approaches to the problem of empirical estimation of costs associated with waste disposal and to the problem of selecting technological alternatives and evaluating their effects.[1]

Some may argue that existing understanding is so limited that any effort to establish a more precise optimizing procedure at this time is futile. Such a conclusion appears unwarranted. It is one of the great attributes of the engineering profession that it has been able to function effectively through application of judgment when only relatively imprecise data are available. Present procedures do not ordinarily attempt an explicit weighing of costs and returns, nor do they provide scope for a full and flexible consideration of alternatives. It seems abundantly clear that a procedure that gives explicit attention to these factors—even when the data are relatively crude—should constitute an improvement over the present situation.

It may be argued that the provision of accurate data will entail too great a cost. Deciding how much to invest in research, data collection, and analysis poses a difficult problem. However, substantial investment in these activities appears warranted in view of the enormous costs already associated with waste disposal and the amounts being invested and contemplated for waste disposal facilities. Furthermore, modern techniques of collection and analysis permit the utilization of large quantities of data at relatively low cost. A number of highly promising studies to develop methodology and information are under way.[2]

---

[1] Allen V. Kneese, *Water Pollution: Economic Aspects and Research Needs* (Washington: Resources for the Future, Inc., 1962).

[2] See particularly chapters 2, 4, and 5 above where some of these studies are indicated.

The most difficult problems of measurement relate to those uses which normally are not assigned a value by the market system or for which willingness to pay cannot be readily imputed. Outdoor recreation use of water and aesthetic and public health considerations are the significant ones. There is considerable promise in the results that have been obtained to date that research will produce increasingly accurate measures of recreational value quite commensurable with other aspects of benefit-cost analysis.[3] Nevertheless, a solution may require a relatively long time. Until this problem is solved—and for those aspects which may never be solved—some other technique of value measurement is required under any optimizing procedure.

In a democratic society we must look to the political process for an answer. This implies that instead of specifying an arbitrary standard of water quality for these purposes, the agency responsible for water quality management would present for public consideration an analysis of the costs of obtaining alternative water quality standards. Responding to its interpretation of the public interest, the politically responsible officials of the agency would then decide upon an appropriate standard. Such standards would then constitute a constraint in the detailed design of the optimizing system and help supply the basis for the assessment of effluent charges, payments, or direct regulation of waste discharges in ways outlined in previous chapters.

Differing Regional Situations

Implicit in any optimizing procedure is the need for adapting the system to the regional situation. If effluent standards are used they cannot be uniform for the nation because appropriate standards vary with the costs of reducing waste discharge, with the demand for water use, and with streamflow conditions, as would effluent charges or payments. A region with a large streamflow can assimilate more wastes than a region with a much smaller flow. Where the demands for water

[3] See Marion Clawson, *Methods of Measuring the Demand for and Value of Outdoor Recreation*, Reprint No. 10 (Washington: Resources for the Future, Inc., February, 1959); Jack Knetsch, "Outdoor Recreation Demands and Benefits," *Land Economics*, November, 1963; and Robert K. Davis, "The Economics of Recreational Development in the Maine Woods" (Ph.D. Thesis, Harvard University, 1963).

are not great, the external costs imposed through lower water quality are not as great as where the demands are large. Also opportunities for large-scale measures and their cost will differ from region to region and thus "trade off" differently against alternatives at individual points of waste generation. For this reason too, the optimal level of waste discharge reduction will differ from region to region. Thus the system must be tailored to the region.

This is not easy because each governmental jurisdiction—local, state, or federal—tends toward uniformity within its jurisdiction. It is not easy to explain why one city or plant should produce one quality of effluent and another city or plant in the same jurisdiction is permitted to meet a lower standard. If a charges system were used— an alternative which in the view of this study compares favorably with effluent standards—differing schedules of charges would be appropriate at different locations within the same basin, and certainly they would vary greatly over the nation.

Complications and opportunities are presented by the desire of the national government to provide leadership in dealing with the pollution problem. How can federal leadership be provided while at the same time taking appropriate account of these regional differences? Possible solutions to this problem are discussed later in this chapter.

Establishing Appropriate Governmental Jurisdictions

In the literature on water resources administration it has been emphasized that the geographic boundaries of governmental jurisdictions are not appropriate for water resources administration. Over the years we have sought to meet this problem through a federal river basin agency (TVA), regionally organized federal agencies, interagency river basin committees and commissions, and now a state-federal basin agency—the Delaware River Basin Commission.

Only an agency with considerable authority can implement an optimizing system that incorporates direct planning and operation of facilities, where merited, and control of individual waste discharges. When a region falls entirely within a single state, such authority can readily be granted under state law. For interstate regions it would appear that such authority could be provided by a federal agency under federal law, or by an interstate or state-federal agency under a compact.

Selection of a Region of Appropriate Size

What constitutes a region in which interdependencies are sufficiently large to imply centralized management? Is it the Muskingum, the Ohio, or the Mississippi? A smaller region like the Muskingum would be more manageable, but there is no doubt that the consequences of water use within a tributary basin will be felt well beyond.

In each instance it must be determined what the interdependencies are and what area they cover. Then an effort must be made to delineate an appropriate management unit on this basis. The final solution probably can only be found through experimentation. In proceeding, it would appear wise not to delay action in heavily developed smaller and medium-sized basins while agreement on appropriate machinery for a larger region is being sought.

In practice it might not be desirable to incorporate all traceable interdependencies in a single managerial unit. Some decentralization can be maintained by permitting separate regional agencies to provide one another with inducements to efficiency. For example, a main-stem authority might treat a tributary under the jurisdiction of a separate agency much like an effluent outfall by specifying a standard for waters entering the main stem and/or levying a charge upon the materials contained in such water. The charges or standards should in principle be set to reflect the incremental main-stem costs of damages, extra treatment, flow regulation, etc., that are attributable to the residual waste load carried by the tributary. In this way the tributary authority would have an incentive to take main-stem costs into account, even though they are not directly within its jurisdiction.

Relationship to Other Water Resources Activities

The efficient use of water supplies for waste disposal cannot be disassociated from the development of water resources for other uses. Waste discharge imposes costs upon most other water uses, and water quality may be improved or reduced as a result of the way a river sys-

tem is managed for a variety of purposes. For example, controlled releases of water in storage for hydroelectric power or navigation may
augment low streamflows and increase the capacity of a stream to
absorb wastes. Or an irrigation development, by reducing the flow of a
stream and by contributing a more saline return flow, may adversely
affect the quality of the water resource. Thus water quality management is inextricably related to the total management of the hydrologic
unit. Yet, we have generally treated it as a separate activity.

How can water quality management be integrated with the over-all
development of the river system? From an administrative standpoint
the simplest procedure would be to combine water quality management responsibilities with other water development and use responsibilities in a single public regional agency. The Delaware River Basin
Commission evidently has such broad authority. For the most part,
however, water quality management responsibilities are separated from
other water development responsibilities at both the federal and state
levels of government.

An alternative to the consolidated regional agency is a separate
regional water quality management agency. An agency of this kind
would need to be in a position to "buy" certain services from the
general water development agencies, such as the maintenance of
certain minimum flow conditions. Such an arrangement would not be
as simple to administer as the single agency, but in some instances
it might be more practicable of attainment. Essentially the relation
between the agencies created for different purposes would be similar
to that outlined earlier between agencies with different but interdependent areal jurisdictions.

Existing Policies

While it is not a purpose of this volume to provide a critique of
existing policies, it is necessary to point out that they are generally not
fully consistent with the development of efficient waste disposal systems. This is because these policies have not been explicitly designed
to optimize, although this is their general objective. They will not be
easy to change in part because there is a natural reluctance to change

and in part because there are groups that have a special interest in the continuation of existing policies.

Existing policies depend primarily upon regulatory actions by state and federal agencies for their implementation. Even if an optimizing system is to rely on regulatory techniques to control waste discharge, it would be necessary to alter existing regulations by designing a separate system for each region. A systematic adoption of payments or charges would, of course, be a large departure from existing practice. The system of charges, because of its advantages, should by no means be ruled out because at first glance it appears rather unorthodox.

Also, it would probably be necessary to alter existing low-flow augmentation policies of the federal government. Under an optimizing system, flow augmentation should be used only when and to the degree that it is the least-cost alternative in the optimizing process. Present policies inhibit a full and flexible consideration of this alternative by specifying comparatively arbitrary conditions for its provision and more or less automatically providing it when these are met. Moreover, non-reimbursability policy for flow augmentation fails to provide appropriate incentives for use of other alternatives. This is especially true of such important possibilities as industrial process changes and waste recovery.

Present policies and procedures provide insufficient opportunity for systematic identification and evaluation in a regional context of opportunities like artificial reaeration of streams, in-stream treatment, treatment of entire streams, collective treatment of diverse wastes from diverse sources, etc. The case study in chapter 7 indicates the important and efficient role which these procedures have played in water quality management in the Ruhr area of Germany.

Leadership in Implementation

The implementation of an optimizing system for waste disposal and water supply in any region would involve, essentially, four major steps. The first step would be to establish an agency with adequate authority to implement such a system. As previously noted, this could be done under state law for an intrastate region, under federal law, or through an interstate compact arrangement. The second step would be to assemble and analyze the data bearing upon the costs of waste disposal in the region. The third step would be to design the system and the program of implementation on the basis of the information that has been assembled and analyzed. The final step would be the implementation of the system. This no doubt would be done progressively over a considerable period, depending upon the complexity of the problems involved. Once the appropriate institution is established, the planning and operation of the system would presumably become a continuous process adaptable to changes in technology and the improved information which would result from the passage of time. Indeed a major advantage of a continuing regional institution would be its adaptability and, in a broad sense, its ability to learn from experience.

Since water quality management now falls largely in the province of state and local governments, state governments are in an excellent position to establish appropriate institutions, especially in the tributary basins which often lie within an individual state. State agencies can readily be provided with the requisite authority to institute one of the three systems described above, or variations thereof. For interstate streams, operating agencies can be established through interstate compact. In view of the large number of tributary basins which lie within a single state, or at most involve only two states, state governments are in an excellent position to exercise considerable leadership in dealing with water quality management problems.

A question arises as to what the role of the federal government might appropriately be in this field. Federal leadership could be particularly important in dealing with main-stem conditions on the larger river systems which transcend the boundaries of several states. In such instances interstate compacts establishing effective agencies are more difficult to negotiate. In view of the widespread concern over pollution, it is evident that there will be considerable pressure for federal action to meet the problem even in the less complex situations.

The federal government could, of course, take direct action in this regard. It could set up regional water quality management agencies or over-all regional water resources agencies with water quality management responsibilities. There could be separate entities such as TVA or units of a regionalized federal agency such as proposed by the First

Hoover Commission. There has been so much opposition to arrangements of this nature, for reasons that need not be examined here, that it is questionable that the federal government would be willing to move in this fashion.

An alternative would be for the federal government to establish incentives for the organization and operation of regional agencies either under state law or through interstate compact. Such incentives might be provided in the following manner: Upon creation of an agency with adequate authority to institute an optimizing system the agency would be eligible for a grant of funds to support a share of its operating cost while it assembled and analyzed the pertinent data and designed its specific program. If the federal government is satisfied that the proposed program would meet reasonable optimizing objectives, the agency might be eligible for a grant to assist it with its operating expenses. Such assistance might appropriately be limited to the implementation period—say, five years. During this period it might be possible to set up a workable system of effluent charges. The regional agency might also be made eligible for federal loans for investment in facilities where scale economies can be achieved.

The federal government might wish to approach the water quality management problem in the broader context of water resources development and management. As previously noted, the administration of water quality management activities would be simplified through the integration of such activities with other management functions in a single agency because of the way water quality is influenced by development and use for other purposes. In that event, the federal governmen could provide support of the type described above to regional water resources agencies having general water management responsibilities including quality management. In addition, the federal government could provide support through the regional agency for flood control, navigation, irrigation, power, and recreation on whatever terms such support is provided for these purposes through federal agencies.[4]

---

[4] This is not intended to imply that existing policies governing federal support for these purposes may not quite justifiably be open to question. The point is that if such regional agencies are to exist and be effective they must be able to offer equivalent water development benefits at no greater cost to the region than when such benefits are provided by an existing federal agency. It is unrealistic to expect regional agencies to exist on any other basis.

If regional agencies are established and supported in this manner—especially during the planning and implementation period—the effluent charge system has the attraction of providing a source of revenue to help support their activities on a continuing basis perhaps in conjunction with charges on other beneficiaries of the general management programs. This would help overcome one of the major difficulties which have confronted past efforts to establish non-federal regional water resources agencies.

Other studies have indicated that water supplies available in the United States generally are more than adequate to meet the foreseeable needs of our growing economy.[5] These studies have also indicated that quality degradation could constitute our most serious water problem. To apply technology efficiently to this problem and actually achieve the best use of our water and associated resources will require substantial innovations in public policy relating to water resources management. Through this examination of economic aspects of water quality and some of their implications, it is hoped that the areas meriting further study will be more evident and some basis will have been provided for understanding how public policies in this field might be improved.

[5] See Nathaniel Wollman, *Water Supply and Demand*, United States Senate, Select Committee on National Water Resources, Committee Print No. 32 (Washington: U.S. Government Printing Office, 1960); and Hans H. Landsberg, Leonard L. Fischman, and Joseph L. Fisher, *Resources in America's Future* (Baltimore: The Johns Hopkins Press for Resources for the Future, Inc., 1963), chapter 19.

Index

Activated carbon treatment, 25, 25n, 78

Adversary proceedings, 6: failure to represent value of water uses, 47, 53

Aeration devices: turbine and mobile, 32

Aeration plants: extended for waste treatment, 22, 23, 24, 24n

Aesthetic considerations: and water resources, 18, 19; in Ruhr area, 168; mentioned, 73

Aesthetic values, 71, 72–74, 199: measurement, 73, 73n, 78

Agricultural chemicals in streams, 11

Algae: effect on fish, 19; in domestic water supply, 19; growth and decay, 11, 16, 17, 18; harvesting from oxidation ponds, 24, 24n; in oxidation ponds, 23

Anaerobic conditions, 13

Artificial reaeration of stream, 32, 140: by *Genossenschaften*, 167, 172

Artificial recharge of groundwater, 33: in Ruhr basin, 27n

Automatic monitoring: of streams, 17, 17n, 70, 71, 184; centrally recorded, 71, 71n; importance in system operation, 154; in Ruhr area, 70n, 104n, 168

Bacteria: coliform count, 12, 77; in natural water bodies, 12; pathogenic, 12, 13, 75

Bakersfield, Calif.: use of sewage for irrigation, 33

Baltimore, Md.: industrial use of treated sewage, 26

Basin-wide firm: hypothetical cases to clarify economic principles, 49–53, 54, 125–29

Baumol, William, 38n, 90n, 95n

Bendixson, Thomas W., 27n

Benefit-cost analysis: application to recreational values, 199; and constrained cost minimization, 156–59

Benefits (damages avoided) and costs (cost of treatment), 45, 51: in private market system, 40

Berger, B. Bernard, 76n, 77n

Bethlehem Steel-Baltimore agreement on chloride, 116

Beuscher, Jacob H., 46n

Biological treatment of wastes, 22: Emscher River, 167

BOD (biochemical oxygen demand): defined, 13; effect of algae, 17, 17n; and other factors, 13, 14; reduction by waste treatment, 21, 22, 23; in streams, 16; tests by Emschergenossenschaft, 174–75; of various industrial wastes, 30, 31, 32, 185

Boehnke, Dr., 15n, 182n

Boiteux, M., 70n, 153n

Bowen, Howard R., 51n

Bower, Blair, 138n

Brown, William G., 73n

Buchanan, James M., 55n, 57n, 85n

Bucksteeg, W., 31n, 171n, 177n, 179, 179n, 184, 184n

Burden, Robert P., 16n

THE ECONOMICS OF REGIONAL WATER QUALITY MANAGEMENT
by Allen V. Kneese

designer:	Edward D. King
typesetter:	Vail-Ballou Press
typefaces:	Caledonia, Palatino
printer:	Vail-Ballou Press
paper:	Warren's 1854
binder:	Vail-Ballou Press
cover material:	Columbia Riverside linen